COUNTY
LIBRARIES
AND LEISURE
SERVICE

Charges will be payable at
the Adult rate if this item
is not returned by the
latest date stamped above.

L21B

 SURREY
COUNTY COUNCIL

BOW PORCELAIN
The Collection formed by Geoffrey Freeman

Thomas Frye

A pair of portrait miniatures (enlarged) on ivory, of an unknown lady and gentleman turned slightly to the right, she in white lace cap, trimmed with lavender ribbon, a similar ribbon tying her black lace choker and with large ear-rings, he with grey-powdered hair tied *en queue*, wearing a dove-grey jacket over a light-blue waistcoat trimmed with silver lace, a white cravat to his neck, on shaded grounds, signed T. Frye, 1761 in gold – oval gold mounts.

oval 1½ in high

BOW PORCELAIN

The Collection formed by Geoffrey Freeman

Written and compiled by Anton Gabszewicz
in collaboration with Geoffrey Freeman

Lund Humphries · London

132426 109382 01

First edition 1982
Published by Lund Humphries Publishers Ltd
26 Litchfield Street London WC2

SBN 85331 452 7

Designed by Graham Johnson/Lund Humphries
Printed in Great Britain by Lund Humphries, Bradford

In fond memory of a loving husband and father

Contents

Authors' Preface

My original intention was to put under one private roof a collection of Bow Porcelain containing an example of every piece the factory produced. I quickly realised that because of the enormous number of different pieces this would not be possible within the time available to me. I then lowered my sights and commenced to collect what I hoped would be a visually historical and comprehensive collection of Bow. I trust I have succeeded.

I started the collection in 1973 on my sixty-third birthday. The main part of my self-appointed task was completed by the end of 1980. Since then I have continued to add pieces, though few in number, still with the object of further enhancing the underlying historical theme of the collection.

Collecting, as with so many things, involves acquiring knowledge, which in itself is a continuous living process, subject to change and amendments as new facts come to light.

It is incumbent on me to render thanks to those who have so willingly helped to make the Collection and assisted in the writing of this book: my ever-patient wife, Norah, who has borne with fortitude the continuing disruption to her household; my secretary, Joyce Eglen, for her willingness to work so competently at all times, with enthusiasm and understanding; Hugh Tait, of the British Museum, for affording me the abundance of his knowledge of eighteenth-century porcelain in general, and Bow in particular; Anton Gabszewicz, my co-author, who has so ably produced the Descriptions and Introductory Notes to the various sections; Jo Marshall, of Sotheby's, who kindly corrected the proofs; Mike Maclaren for his excellent photography; Dr Bernard Watney for writing the Foreword; The English Ceramic Circle, that erudite institution from which I have learnt so much; and my main dealer, Robert Williams of Winifred Williams, for discovering most of the exotic pieces.

Geoffrey Freeman

I would particularly like to thank Miss Caroline Williams, for her tireless enthusiasm in typing the Introductory Notes and Descriptions; Graham Johnson of Lund Humphries Printers for his expertise and guidance in preparing the format and layout of this book; Charlotte Burri for her painstaking proof reading and compiling of the index; my colleagues and friends at Christie's and among the porcelain dealing world, my family and especially Mark Gutteridge, who have been a constant support during the birth pangs of this book; lastly, but not least, my most sincere thanks to Geoffrey Freeman, who allowed me to work with him and without whose collection this work would not exist, for his enthusiastic encouragement and kindness and without whose initial descriptions and notes this work would never have been started; my hope is that this book will be a lasting tribute to his Memory.

Geoffrey Freeman had originally intended to include copies of the Bowcock Papers and the Bow Accounts 1750–55 as an integral part of this book. Since his untimely death has intervened, this was no longer possible. However I intend to give a paper to The English Ceramic Circle concerning these and drawing on the Freeman Collection for illustrative examples.

Shortly before his death he had arranged with Anne George of Albert Amor Ltd to lend items from his collection for an exhibition of Bow Porcelain. Happily this exhibition is still to take place in June 1982 to coincide with the publication of this book which he had so eagerly looked forward to.

Anton Gabszewicz

Foreword

Most amateurs when they start collecting must regret that there no longer appear to be the same wonderful opportunities that, they are told, presented themselves several decades earlier. The late Geoffrey Freeman was not in any way inhibited by this. He accepted the situation as he found it in 1973 and with single-minded devotion he proceeded forthwith to build up an incomparable collection of Bow. The fact that fine quality examples of this porcelain were hard to find made him all the more keen, and as a late starter, often in poor health, the immediacy of his quest was given further momentum. Consequently, in less than nine years he did what others would have considered to be well nigh impossible; he formed the wide and representative Bow porcelain collection that is illustrated and recorded in this handsome book. The strengths of his collection are variety and excellence. He acquired many key pieces and he even managed to obtain documentary examples, some previously unrecorded.

The many fellow amateurs who were invited to see his collection were treated to a fine and memorable display, meticulously catalogued, each with a colour photograph and carefully typed description. Nonetheless, I was surprised to discover how many individual items could be recalled as eminently desirable when I came to jot down some impressions following my visit in the late summer of last year. My list included a bowl and two wall pockets in coloured enamels after the sculptural style of Doccia porcelain. An early dolphin salt and a sauceboat with three lion-mask and paw feet and an arched over handle. A splendid teapot with well-fitting lid, painted with bunches of grapes, and a sweetmeat tray, six and a half inches wide, moulded and enamelled with white currants on leaves; a design known on salt glaze and Lowestoft, but previously unrecorded on Bow. A superb and early *Barking Dog* in white showing considerable finishing by hand and a duck tureen every bit as good as Chelsea. A rare Bow rose box with moulded insects delicately over-painted, and a 'Blind Earl' porcelain stand that might have been made for a larger size of rose box as yet unrecorded.

The splendid early 'drab-ware' mug, from the John Ainslie Collection, with a wide spreading, 'beaded-over' base, like a metal example, is matched by another with the same shape, equally rare, but of more orthodox paste and with typical *famille-rose* decoration. His large, robust and early tureens are as typical of the Bow output as are the variety of immensely fine vases of Kakiemon shape and decoration. Then, for contrast compare the strong architecture of the plain white wall bracket, moulded with scales, scrolls and acanthus leaves and the fragile blue and white cream ladle like an acorn cup on a twig. An undecorated bowl and cover flanked by the figure of a negress, from the Meissen, is known from a dated example elsewhere, to have been made around 1750; a fragment of another such decorative piece was found on the factory site.

It would be invidious to draw attention to only a small selection of the human figures, but a favourite primitive is the white *Huntsman Toper* buttressed by a strong overall cone-shape and further strengthened by a cut-out additional layer inside the base in the manner of pastry making. Every Bow figure collector must strive to possess a fine pair of *Cooks*, some *Muse* figures and at least one *Kitty Clive* and a *Woodward*, but who other than Geoffrey Freeman could have obtained in the past few years a pair of *Mongolian* busts, a *Fortune Teller* group, the primitive *Chinese Lovers* in white, three different *Prize-Fighters* and a statuesque figure of *Flora*?

The fine illustrations speak for themselves, but the addition of a carefully researched and accurate catalogue gives to this work an authority and value unrivalled in the literature on Bow.

Bernard Martyn Watney, F.S.A.
President English Ceramic Circle

Some Notes on the Bow Factory

Over the years much has been written about the Bow factory, and these short notes together with the Introductory Notes, the Illustrations and Descriptions of the pieces in the Freeman Collection are only intended to tell the Bow story in outline.

Little is known of the early years before 1750, but it is known with certainty that Thomas Frye, Edward Heylyn and Alderman George Arnold founded the factory before that date.

Thomas Frye (b.1710 near Dublin, d. 2 April 1762) was an artist and mezzotintist of considerable merit. Many of his works are extant. His earliest recorded work is a pastel of a young boy, signed and dated 1734. He painted Frederick, Prince of Wales, for the Saddlers' Company in February 1738. The miniatures illustrated here (frontispiece) are fine yet later examples of his work. It is curious that, as far as is known, he did not paint on one piece of Bow porcelain. It is even more curious that he left the relatively 'soft' world of art for the hard and dangerous world of porcelain, perhaps an indication of the impact porcelain made in the eighteenth century. He was the manager, driving force and artistic inspiration of the factory. Sarah, one of his five children, worked at the factory as a painter. His brother, Henry, may also have been connected with the factory.

Edward Heylyn (b.1695 at Westminster, d. April 1765) lived in Bow from 1753–56. He was a copper merchant and glass manufacturer owning a factory near the Bow site. As far as is known his connection with Bow was from about 1744 until his bankruptcy in 1757, the latter event being possibly the cause of his departure.

Alderman George Arnold (b.1691, d.1751) was a man of considerable wealth with access to finance in the City of London, and shortly before his death provided or secured the original capital which enabled the factory to be built and production in large quantities to commence.

On 6 December 1744, Frye and Heylyn, both then living in Bow, enrolled a Patent for the manufacture of a material in which no clear reference to the manufacture of porcelain was made. It states: '... a new method of manufacturing a certain material whereby a ware might be made of the same nature or kind, and equal to, if not exceeding in goodness and beauty, China or Porcelain ware imported from abroad'. The wording of this Patent is vague, referring only to the manufacturing of a *material*. However, it sets the scene and indicates the intention of the Patentees. Later, in 1748, Frye enrolled a Patent of his own. This clearly indicates the resolve to manufacture porcelain. It states: '... and vend my new method of making ware, which is not inferior to ... China,

Japan or porcelain ware'. Thus, we are now clearly told what were the objectives, i.e. to manufacture porcelain in competition with Chinese and Japanese imports. It is possible that the partners played a part in presenting petitions to Parliament with the object of restricting foreign imports – as then, as now.

The precise materials used at Bow are not known. What is known, however, is that a clay called 'unaker', imported from the American Colonies was used in the early years. It is also known that potash in the form of calcined bone was extensively used. Frye was the first person to use calcined bone in the manufacture of porcelain, thus laying the foundation for bone china as we know it today.

Just prior to 1750 the building of the factory commenced in Stratford Road, Bow, in the County of Essex (now Stratford High Street, New Ham, London). The factory bordered the Bow Back River, fronting Stratford Road, between Bow Bridge and Marshgate Lane, both of which exist today. It is probable that this river was navigable at that time and used for the transportation of the factory's wares. Certainly Bow owned, or chartered, a ship named *The Antelope*. Easy access to the river and proximity to the City of London could well have been two of the reasons why this particular site was chosen.

The name given to the factory was 'New Canton', the exterior design being copied from the East India Warehouse in Canton. Indeed, the famous ink-pots were inscribed 'Made at New Canton' with the date 1750 or 1751 (see footnote to No. 62).

On 7 July 1749, an Insurance Policy was written by the Sun Assurance Company in the names of Edward Heylyn, Thomas Frye, John Weatherby and John Crowther, in the sum of £4,000 covering both buildings and contents. The description of the factory given in this Policy was: '... their China Manufactory in the Stratford Road, in the County of Essex'. It also affords documentary evidence of two more personalities appearing on the scene, Weatherby and Crowther; and evidence that Heylyn, Frye, Weatherby and Crowther were principals, whilst Alderman George Arnold appears to have been a sleeping partner. There seems to be some confusion between the date of the Policy and the date the factory commenced work.

John Weatherby (b. unknown, d. 15 October, 1762) and John Crowther (b. unknown, d. 1790) entered into partnership during or before 1739 to run a successful business dealing in ceramics and glass at their warehouse at St Katherine's by the Tower. This partnership appears to have been a great financial success. They both joined Bow in 1749. In 1753 they also had a warehouse in Cornhill which was sold in 1763/64, the time when Crowther was adjudged bankrupt.

Weatherby and Crowther had connections with Staffordshire. Documentary evidence of this exists in a letter written to them, dated 21 September 1748, by John Wedgwood (the brother of Josiah Wedgwood) and states: 'you remember I cam [sic] in April with Mr. Heath to reconcile Mr. Farmer with Widow Briand; that Mr. Frye and I came to hear what you had to say for or against Mr. Briand touching his behaviour in the making of china. And so I believe you gave but ill character of him in it . . .'. The letter clearly shows that both Weatherby and Crowther knew Frye in 1748.

The warehouse at Cornhill was in operation from 1753–63. In 1753 a Mr John Bowcock (b. unknown, d.1765) was appointed Manager, Clerk and general factotum. He was a man of parts, possessed with considerable business acumen, some-time sailor, connected with the Ravenhead Collieries in St Helens, Lancashire, the Warrington Glass Company and the Warrington Wholesale and Retail Warehouse, selling among other items 'Blue, Green, White and Painted Enamels'.

Much documentary evidence of the factory and its personalities is to be found in the Bowcock Papers, now in the British Museum, Department of Medieval & Later Antiquities. The Accounts for the years 1750–54, in the British Library, Department of Manuscripts (Additional Mss. 45905), afford us detailed evidence of the factory's transactions. The Accounts for the year 1754 show a turnover of £18,715. 8s. 9d. – an enormous amount at that time. This huge amount taken together with the potted history given by Thomas Craft, and the information within the Insurance Policies, proves with certainty that Bow was the largest porcelain factory in England, and possibly in Europe, during the eighteenth century.

Thomas Craft (b. unknown, d. some time after 1790) was a talented painter working at the factory. His name appears in the St Mary Stratford Langthorne Parish Register for 1756. Craft's potted history of the factory is illustrated on the back of the jacket of this book, taken from the underside of the lid of the box containing the famous Craft bowl.

Not only was the factory large, it produced a very wide variety of pieces including useful wares, vases and ornaments, figures and animals. Most were decorated in the factory, some by outside decorators such as James Giles, William Duesbury and Richard Dyer. All were made in an amazing profusion and variety within each type in polychrome, monochrome, white, underglaze-blue, over and underglaze transfers; possibly some were purpose-made and sold in the biscuit. All, with the exception of biscuit, are represented in the Freeman Collection.

Samuel Richardson, in his 4th edition of Daniel Defoe's *Tour of Great Britain*, vol. 1, p. 2, states: '. . . the first village we come to is Bow, where a large Manufactory of Porcelaine is lately set up. They have already made large quantities of Tea-cups, etc. which by some skilful persons are said to be little inferior to those which are brought from China. If they can work this, so as to undersell the Foreign Porcelaine, it may become a profitable Business to the Undertakers, and save great sums to the Public, which are annually sent abroad for this Commodity'. Richardson's account of Defoe's *Tour* also provides evidence that work had commenced at Bow at least by 1748.

The famous Victorian collector, Lady Charlotte Schreiber, in her *Journal* (published by her son, Montague Guest, see Bibliography) mentions a number of pieces of Bow purchased by her in Europe, thus indicating that Bow had a thriving export business to the Continent. There is also documentary evidence of the factory exporting to the Colonies of America – still more proof of the factory's success.

Unfortunately we are unable to arrive at precise dates for the opening and closing of the factory, but we can say with reasonable certainty that it was in operation for about 29 years.

The Bowcock Papers provide evidence that the factory was in operation in 1749 under the name of 'Ald. Arnold & Co.'. An indication of the closing date is provided after Frye retired in 1759 (owing to ill health) and Bowcock's death in 1765. This evidence is to be found in two Insurance Policies dated Christmas 1766 and Christmas 1767, both written in the name of John Crowther only. Thus, it would seem, Crowther carried on the business from then onwards until the closure. Some writers opine that on the closure of the factory, the moulds, implements, etc. were purchased by Willian Duesbury and removed to Derby. No contemporary documentary evidence of this has yet come to light.

Geoffrey Freeman

PLATE I Wide cylindrical mug, 1747–50 (No. 1)

PLATE II Compressed cylindrical teapot and cover, *c.* 1754 (No. 17)

PLATE III Lobed oval teapot and cover, *c.* 1753 (No. 51)

PLATE IV Cylindrical ink-pot, *c.* 1760 (No. 62)

PLATE V Circular tureen and domed cover, *c.* 1750 (No. 75)

PLATE VI Two views of a pear-shaped bottle, *c.* 1765 (No. 163)

PLATE VII Oval pierced two-handled basket and cover, *c.* 1765 (No. 161)

PLATE VIII Figure of Urania, 1750–52 (No. 200)

PLATE IX A selection of animals; from left to right: stag (No. 250), two monkeys (No. 260), dismal hound (No. 255), cock and hen (No. 266), c. 1755–60

PLATE X A tea-party group, c. 1760 (No. 232)

Concerning Dating

The whole question of placing a particular item within the known dates of a factory's period of production has always been fraught with enormous difficulties and Bow has been no exception. My conclusions have been based on both reference to other works (mentioned in the Bibliography) and endless discussion with friends whose interest in Bow has similarly led them to more detailed observation. In preparing this book I have been in the privileged position of handling each piece many times and, since Geoffrey Freeman's wish was to have the collection listed chronologically, it seemed an ideal opportunity to reconsider the problem of dating.

Elizabeth Adams's work on the Bow Insurances, published in the *E.C.C. Transactions*, vol. 9, pt. 1, pp. 67–108, followed by her later book in conjunction with David Redstone: *Bow Porcelain* (see Bibliography), has shown how prolific Bow's production was, especially in the 1750s. In Appendix V of the above work, it is clear from these Insurances that Bow was commercially well ahead of Worcester, whose *stock and utensils* in 1757 were valued at £2,000 whereas Bow's *stock and utensils* in late 1755 were valued at £5,900. These figures, although taken out of context, suggest that products of the Bow factory were at that time more readily available than those from Worcester. Today, over 200 years later, this is indeed surprising since more pieces of Worcester have survived the ravages of time than Bow. Some explanation is needed for this and I think it lies in the fact that Bow was perhaps the first factory to have attracted a wider market. In the early 1750s porcelain production was in its infancy in England. The Chinese export wares, the Japanese porcelains and the European wares of Meissen and, to a lesser extent, St Cloud and Chantilly were imported for the titled, rich and landed classes. Bow's rivals, Chelsea and Worcester, were both capturing the same market and, at that date, made little attempt to produce wares for the 'man in the street'. Many of the wares from these English factories were intended for the rich man's table or they were placed in his 'cabinet of curiosities', and as a result they were always treasured and carefully looked after. Bow, on the other hand, although it certainly did produce wares equal in excellence to the output of these other factories, also manufactured enormous quantities of everyday ware. This can be seen especially in the area of blue and white, where the paste lent itself to the making of plates and dishes, an area where Worcester was not successful until the mid 1760s and where Chelsea, in blue and white, made little attempt to compete. It can therefore be seen that Bow was operating a two-tier scheme of production appealing to all classes and sections of contemporary society; therein lay their success, a success that apparently continued until Worcester was able to produce more readily available underglaze-blue wares and their successful ground colours (the rich man's alternative to Chelsea, then in its declining years) in the mid to late 1760s.

The foregoing remarks, though not immediately concerned with the dating of individual pieces, partly explain why there is more Bow porcelain from the 1750s and early 1760s, than in the later 1760s and 1770s.

To turn now to the question of dating. I have relied heavily on contemporary references, especially the Bowcock Papers, which give a clear indication of what was being produced in 1756 and also the known dated pieces and I make no apologies for listing these again as I feel they are extremely useful foundations on which to base a dating system. The trap I have tried hard to avoid is that of dating based on these factors alone and I have therefore combined this evidence with observation of the paste and glaze of the objects and consideration of whether items similar in form and decoration are known at other factories. This, I appreciate, can be extremely dangerous and misleading and explains why I have adopted the two systems, i.e. first, using '*c.* 1750' when I think an object was made in or about that year and second, '1747–50' when the earliest and latest probable dates are ascertainable with a fair degree of certainty using the criteria above. Where I feel additional information is needed as explanation, this can be found in the Introductory Notes to each section or in the footnotes beneath the Descriptions of the objects being considered.

In conclusion, I realise that to a certain extent my attributions must be a matter of individual opinion but my hope is that my comments will be a help rather than a hindrance to future students of Bow porcelain.

Anton Gabszewicz
Pimlico, 1982

Dated Wares and Documentary Pieces

The numbers in brackets refer to Hugh Tait's Catalogue of the special Exhibition of Documentary Material at the British Museum 1959–60 (*Bow Porcelain 1744–1776*)

1750 Ink-pot: 'MADE AT NEW CANTON 1750' – underglaze-blue with pagodas and shrubs – Colchester Museum (20)

   Ink-pot: 'MADE AT NEW CANTON 1750' – enamelled with prunus and banded hedges – British Museum (9)

   Ink-pot: 'MADE AT NEW CANTON 1750' – as above – Salisbury & South Wiltshire Museum

   Ink-pot: 'MADE AT NEW CANTON 1750' – as above – Fitzwilliam Museum, Cambridge

   Bowl: 'WILLIAM AND ELIZABETH MARTIN, NOVEMBER 20, 1750' – underglaze-blue with shrubs from pierced rockwork – British Museum (26)

   White shell salt: incised date on the base – British Museum (32)

   Kitty Clive: white – Fitzwilliam Museum (40)

   Henry Woodward: white – Untermyer Collection, Metropolitan Museum, New York (42)

   Negress with a basket: white – Museum of Fine Arts, Boston (Katz Collection) (44) cf. Freeman Collection No. 184

1751 Ink-pot: 'MADE AT NEW CANTON 1751' – enamelled as above – Victoria & Albert Museum (14)

1752 Ink-pot: 'EDWARD BERMINGHAM 1752' – underglaze-blue – British Museum (28)

   Ink-pot: 'E(D)WARD VERNON Esqr. JULY 1752' – underglaze-blue – with figures among pagodas and rockwork – Brighton Museum and Art Gallery (30)

1754 Flower-pot: 'THOMAS AND ANN TARGET JULY 2th 1754' – famille rose enamels and prunus moulding – British Museum (62)

   Bowl: 'THO^S: TARGET 1754' – Chinese figures in landscapes, enamelled in green, blue, brown and maroon with overpainting in gold – Formerly Dr John Ainslie (64)

   Cream-jug: 'W. PETHER MAY 10 1754' – underglaze-blue bamboo and rockwork by a fence – Dr B. Watney Collection (81)

   Cream-jug: 'A. TARGET 1754' – similarly painted to the preceding in famille rose enamels – Clifford J. Larsen Collection

   Teabowl: 'ANN TARGET 1754' – *en suite* to the cream-jug above – private collection, Virginia

   Bowl: date 1754 – underglaze-blue – Freeman Collection No. 85

1757   Mug: 'EPEC 1757' – underglaze-blue, figures in a romantic garden with an urn and ruined temple – British Museum (91)

Bagpiper: inscribed I.B. 1757 – enamelled on the instrument (101)

1759   Bowl: 'JOHN AND ANN BOWCOCK 1759' – powder-blue and underglaze-blue – British Museum (125)

Mug: 'Wm. TAYLOR 1759' – enamelled bouquets and swags of flowers – Victoria & Albert Museum (103)

Handel vase: commemorating Handel's death – British Museum (104) cf. Freeman Collection No. 138

Handel clock-case: inscribed 'Nov. 5th 1759' – Freeman Collection No. 139

1760   The Craft bowl: enamelled with swags of flowers and with floral monogram of Thomas Craft in the centre, in a cardboard box with a written inscription dating the bowl to 1760 – British Museum (111 and 112)

1761   Teapot: 'I. ^C G. 1761' – enamelled exotic birds and flowers on a blue scale ground – The Glynn Vivian Art Gallery, Swansea (106)

Bowl: 'JOHN AND ELIZAB^{H.} ROBERTS 1761' – enamelled fruit and flowers – Untermyer Collection, Metropolitan Museum, New York (105)

1762   Mug: 'MRS. ANN AMBLER 1762' – underglaze-blue with butterflies and cell-pattern borders, ribbed – National Museum of Wales, Cardiff (129)

Bowl: 'MR. JOHN CHAPMAN 1762' – enamelled fruit and flowers – Freeman Collection No. 154

1763   Coffee-cup: 'I.C. 1763' – underglaze-blue flowers – Formerly Dr John Ainslie (131)

1767   Bowl: 'HALLIFAX-LODGE NORTH-CAROLINA' – enamelled flowers and exotic birds on a green ground – Museum of Early Southern Decorative Arts, Winston-Salem, North Carolina, USA (dated invoice still extant)

Bowl: 'LIBERTY' – enamelled with fruit on a green ground, similar to the preceding – Freeman Collection No. 172

Mug: 'S ^T E 1767' – underglaze-blue arms of the Carpenters' Company

1770   Mug: 'This Pint was Painted for Mrs. Mary Bromley of Campden Gloc^{shire} by her Loving Son John De Lanauze January 1770' – enamelled with a turbanned man smoking a pipe and a shepherd and shepherdess – British Museum (120)

Mug: 'IOSEPH & MARGRET PENNYFEAT(H)^{ER} April 1770' – underglaze-blue pagodas and wooded river islands, a floral border with the initials 'I.^{P.}M.' – Victoria & Albert Museum (140)

Plates: 'MR. ROBERT CROWTHER STOCKPORT CHESHIRE, January 1770' – underglaze-blue 'RC' monogram in a floral scroll cartouche with an elaborate cell and foliage border – British Museum and Fitzwilliam Museum (139)

Wares with 'Famille Rose' Decoration

The earliest coloured wares that have been attributed to the Bow factory bear delicate 'famille rose' drawing inspired by the Chinese export porcelain, first made in the 1730s, when this palette with its preponderance of pink and aubergine became the fashion and replaced the 'famille verte' palette that had been popular from the end of the seventeenth century. The new style quickly gained favour in England, especially at Bow, where the factory helped to establish its popularity and with it achieved a commercial success that lasted for some fifteen years.

Although this type of painting is based mainly on the simple formulae of chrysanthemum and peony issuing from rockwork, or simple scattered flowers or trailing branches, it falls into several distinct categories. The earliest version, perhaps, can be seen on the mug (No. 1) and the baluster mugs (Nos. 10 and 11); note especially the combination of iron-red and purple used in broad washes which leave wet-looking areas on the petals, and note also the foliage which is generally outlined in brown enamel. The objects from this early period are for the most part of the well-documented 'drab' variety having a glaze of mushroom-grey appearance. These show a remarkable sophistication for what are generally considered to be the earliest wares, marginally pre-dating the New Canton ink-pots of 1750–51, whose palette is wetter and more vivid. The mugs are robustly potted, sometimes with flared bases and thick scroll handles with mask terminals (a feature that can be seen too on the sauceboats Nos. 25 and 26 and also the white candlesticks No. 33). The sauceboats are of graceful silver form, No. 7 with its C-scroll handle being especially successful and illustrating how aesthetically pleasing these earliest wares can be. The salts of both three-shell and single form (Nos. 3, 5 and 2) are crisply moulded on rockwork bases applied with small shells and with grey-green encrustations of a peculiar tone. The borders are usually in a dark-brown, either a single line or, as on the mugs, a precisely pencilled scroll border simply relieved by flowerheads or tent-shaped intrusions.

Some wares towards the end of this earliest period bear an incised line or R mark, the significance of which is not clear, although it has been suggested that perhaps these items were selected for some special treatment; certainly the imposing vase and cover (No. 9) must be considered a triumph of both the potter's and decorator's art, perhaps from a garniture like the gilt and white vase (No. 34) which also bears an incised R mark. On grounds of form and style, these wares seem to date from 1750–52. The mug (No. 13) is beginning to lose the precise style of pre-1750 painting, the palette is wetter, the potting less robust; the border is becoming more complex with green diaper-pattern and panels of flowerheads, while the handle is now of a grooved loop form with a triangular terminal, a forerunner of the heart-shaped terminal which was to become a typical feature at Bow in the later 1750s. The double-salt (No. 15) illustrates the problem of dating rather well; the border of tight foliage and flowers (reminiscent of the Target flower-pot) with pink on the outside suggests a slightly later date than the form, which links up with the other shells previously mentioned and with the bright palette indicates a half-way date of *c.* 1752.

The 'prunus-moulded' wares with enamel flowers are deliberately included here as they show how Bow quickly exploited the simple white wares by enhancing them at little expense and widening their appeal. The sugar-bowl and cover (No. 21) with Kakiemon flowers has an incised R mark and is early in comparison with the teabowl and saucer (No. 30) which, with its muddy green and careless painting, seems to be of about 1755, if not later. The teapots (Nos. 17 and 18) and the following wares with trailing vine, although slightly out of line with the main group, all have marked similarities with the Target bowl dated 1754, illustrating how this link between form and decoration with dated pieces can be so useful.

From about 1755 the range widened but this led to the production of debased copies of their forerunners, both in form and decoration. Oriental figures became a popular idiom, as will be seen later, where an altogether brighter, opaque and less subtle palette of turquoise, yellow and pink was used, more typically associated with Bow of a slightly later period. Outline printing was also introduced commercially, and these designs were washed-in, in a similar palette and are discussed under the transfer-printed section.

1 Wide cylindrical mug 1747–50
with flared base, the thick double-scroll
handle with mask terminal, painted in a
precise famille rose palette with iron-red,
pink, yellow and blue flowering branches
with foliage in two tones of green, the base
with trailing flowering branches, the interior
rim with tight C-scrolls and flowerheads, all
beneath a drab glaze.
5¼ in high

Provenance:
Dr John Ainslie, sale Sotheby's, 7 March
1961, lot 158

Literature:
Bow Porcelain Exhibition Catalogue, 1959, fig. 2
Adams (Elizabeth) and David Redstone: *Bow
Porcelain*, pl. 41

1

2 A pair of shell salts 1747–50
painted in a bright famille rose palette with
pink and blue flowers with yellow centres
and with grey-green leaves within a brown
line rim, the exteriors deeply incised and
with trailing flowering branches, on rockwork
bases applied with grey-green seaweed and
white shells, all beneath a drab glaze.
3½ in wide

Provenance:
Frank Hurlbutt, sale Sotheby's, 11 April
1946, part lot 9

Literature:
Hurlbutt (Frank): *Bow Porcelain*, p. 95, pl.
16b

2

3 A three-shell salt 1747–50
the interiors painted with bright-blue, iron-
red and yellow scattered flowers and
flowerheads, the deeply fluted exteriors with
trailing flowering branches and blue
flowerheads, the rockwork base applied with
pink shells and grey-green seaweed,
surmounted by green seaweed, three short
branches of coral and three pink shells.
5 in wide

Cf. Adams (Elizabeth) and David Redstone: *Bow Porcelain*,
col. pl. C

3

4 Shell-salt 1747–50
the fluted shell painted in a wet famille rose
palette with dark puce and blue flowerheads
with yellow centres, supported by a deeply
scaled dolphin with gaping mouth and
applied with deep blue and puce flowers with
foliage in tones of green, on a pierced oval
rockwork base, beneath a drab glaze, *small
numeral 2 mark in black enamel.*
5½ in wide

The pair to the present example is in the British Museum

4

5 A three-shell salt 1747–50
the interiors painted in green with red and
yellow flowers, the undersides deeply fluted
and with scattered trailing branches and
flowerheads, on a rockwork base applied with
white shells and green seaweed, surmounted
by seaweed and further shells.
7 in wide

5

6 A triangular shell salt *c.* 1750
the interior painted with elongated leaves in
tones of green and pink, and blue flowers
with blue and yellow centres, within a border
of blue and pink flowerheads within a grey
line rim, the fluted exterior edged in puce,
resting on a triangular rockwork base applied
with coloured shells and green seaweed.
4½ in wide

Provenance:
Anon., sale Phillips, 7 November 1979, lot
164

Literature:
Tait (Hugh): 'The Bow Factory Under
Alderman Arnold and Thomas Frye
(1747–1759)' – *E.C.C. Transactions*, vol. 5, pt.
4, pl. 192

6

7 Lobed oval sauceboat 1747–50
the C-scroll handle with blue foliage terminal
and with three lion-mask and small paw feet,
painted in a bold palette with iron-red roses
and pink flowers with yellow centres, the
interior similarly painted within an iron-red
diaper-pattern border.
8¼ in long

Although this piece is unmarked, it would seem to belong
quite firmly within the 'incised R' group. There is a
marked teapot with very similar decoration in a private
collection

Cf. Adams (Elizabeth) and David Redstone: *Bow Porcelain*,
pl. 43 for a sauceboat of similar form with Imari type
decoration

7

8 Flat hexagonal sauceboat *c.* 1750
with stylised serpent handle, the foliage-
moulded exterior painted in a wet famille
rose palette with puce trailing flowers with
blue and green foliage in two tones, the
interior similarly painted, the centre with a
flower-spray.
5½ in long

Provenance:
Anon., sale Phillips, 11 March 1981, lot 80

For this form of sauceboat, more frequently found in blue
and white, cf. Watney (Bernard): *English Blue and White
Porcelain of the 18th Century*, pl. 6D

For painting of similar type cf. *E.C.C. Exhibition Catalogue,
1977*, pl. 13b

8

9 Large baluster vase and domed cover *c.* 1750

painted in a rich famille rose palette with trailing prunus and finger citrus issuing from blue rockwork, the reverse with a phoenix above a plant, the shoulder with two lobed panels painted *en grisaille* with houses beneath willow trees, the cover similarly painted, the finial enriched in blue, *incised line mark*.

13 in high

Provenance:

W. Winkworth Collection

Senator Donovan Collection

Anon., sale Sotheby's, 23 October 1979, lot 194

Literature:

Adams (Elizabeth) and David Redstone: *Bow Porcelain*, col. pl. D

Although the attribution of this piece has been held in doubt (see G. Morazzoni/S. Levy: *Le Porcellane Italiane*, vol. 1, pl. 70 where it is attributed to Cozzi) perhaps on the grounds of style and glaze it should be compared with the vases and covers in the Victoria & Albert Museum (*Schreiber Collection Catalogue*, pl. 12, no. 37) and also The Broderip Gift Vase C1246A-1924

9

10

11

12

13

14

10 A pair of baluster mugs *c.* 1750
with angular strap handles with curved
terminals, painted in a pale wet palette with
three flowers in puce and red with yellow
centres suspended from swags of turquoise
foliage outlined in brown, from a brown line
rim with ribbon-pattern, the interior rim in
dark-brown with tight scrolls and
flowerheads, *incised line to one base and painter's
numeral 7 beneath the handle.*
4¾ in high

Cf. No. 11 for a mug painted in a similar palette

11 Baluster mug *c.* 1750
the grooved handle with kick terminal,
similarly painted to the preceding but with a
brighter blue and the addition of brown
moths and bees and with a plain scroll
border.
5¼ in high

Provenance:
Dr John Ainslie, sale Sotheby's, 7 March
1961, lot 159

Cf. No. 10

12 Wide cylindrical mug *c.* 1752
with flared base and thick scroll handle, the
terminal with a mask, painted in a wet
famille rose palette with puce, bright yellow
and blue flowers issuing from pale-mauve
pierced rockwork beneath a green diaper-
pattern border reserved with puce
flowerheads.
4¾ in high

Cf. No. 1

13 Flared cylindrical mug *c.* 1752
the grooved loop handle with triangular-
shaped terminal painted in a wet famille rose
palette with pink chrysanthemum issuing
from washed brown pierced rockwork and
with foliage in two tones of green, beneath a
green diaper-pattern and pink flowerhead
border, *incised R mark and other incised marks.*
5½ in high

Provenance:
Frank Arnold, sale Sotheby's, 28 January
1964, lot 221
Anon., sale Christie's, 3 February 1975, lot
144

14 Flared cylindrical mug *c.* 1752
with grooved loop handle, painted with a wet
brush in bright pink, yellow and blue with
flowering shrubs with foliage in two tones of
green, beneath a brown cell-pattern border
reserved with flowerheads and edged with
yellow strapwork, *iron-red dagger mark.*
4¾ in high

Provenance:
Frank Arnold

Cf. a similarly painted baluster mug formerly in the Dr
John Ainslie Collection, sale Sotheby's, 7 March 1961, lot
160

15 A double-salt *c.* 1752
formed as two irregularly shaped shells
painted in a bright famille rose palette with
trailing flowering branches within a border of
tightly scrolling foliage and flowerheads
divided by three branches of coral on a
pierced rockwork base applied with coral,
seaweed and coloured shells.
8¼ in wide

Provenance:
Anon, sale Sotheby's, 26 November 1974, lot
145

15

16 Centrepiece 1753–55
modelled as six shell-moulded stirrup-cups
painted in a bright famille rose palette with
trailing flowers, supported on a pierced
rockwork base applied with coloured shells,
seaweed and coral, about a central support
with three bird's nests containing one, two
and three speckled eggs respectively,
surmounted by a pale-yellow whelk.
7½ in wide

Provenance:
Anon, sale Sotheby's, 12 March 1974, lot 137

Cf. Watney (Bernard): *English Blue and White Porcelain of
the 18th Century*, pl. 9A for a blue and white example
formerly in the Ainslie Collection. For another coloured
example, cf. the *Bow Porcelain Exhibition Catalogue, 1959*, no.
71. Also *Apollo* August 1958 where the then three other
recorded examples are described

16

17 Compressed cylindrical teapot and cover *c.* 1754

with short curved spout and thick loop handle, painted in a raised famille rose palette with an allover pattern of trailing vine, the grapes in tones of puce, the leaves in tones of green, the brown branches outlined in gilding, *the base and cover with painter's numeral 10.*

4¼ in high

It is interesting to note that there are marked similarities between this teapot and The Thomas Target Bowl, dated 1754, in the British Museum (formerly in the Ainslie Collection) especially in the use of puce 'berries' and the combination of brown enamel with gold

17

18 Large globular teapot and cover

c. 1754

painted with the 'Target Pattern' depicting a blue-clothed figure crossing a puce bridge between washed green and brown islands enriched in gilding, with further brown islands with pagodas in the distance, surrounded by boulders enriched in gilding.

5½ in high

Provenance:
Anon., sale Sotheby's, 27 April 1976, lot 102

Cf. Tilley (Frank): *Teapots and Tea*, pl. XXI, no. 70 for a similar example. Also The Target Bowl (1754), formerly in the Ainslie Collection, illustrated in the *Bow Porcelain Exhibition Catalogue, 1959*, figs. 25–27, no. 64

18

19 Saucer-dish *c.* 1754
painted in underglaze-blue and overglaze
black, puce and gilding, with an allover
pattern of asymmetrical trailing vine with
blue and gilt tendrils.
6 in diam.

Cf. Klaber & Klaber: *Oriental Influences on European
Porcelain*, nos. 20 and 20A
Hurlbutt (Frank): *Bow Porcelain*, pl. 16A for similar
examples of this pattern
Also No. 20
The pattern also occurs on Worcester porcelain, cf.
Marshall (H. Rissik): *Coloured Worcester Porcelain of The
First Period*, pl. 12, no. 217A

19

20 Flared teabowl and saucer *c.* 1754
painted in grey and puce, black and gilding
with an asymmetric pattern of trailing vine,
the teabowl with black numeral 10.

Cf. Dr John Ainslie, sale Sotheby's, 7 March 1961, lot 27,
for an example of the same pattern using underglaze-blue
as with No. 19

20

21 Sugar-bowl and cover *c.* 1752
applied with prunus branches with two
open and three half-open flowers divided by
three flowerheads and painted in blue, iron-
red and tones of green with flower-sprays and
foliage, the cover with acorn finial, *incised R
mark and 32 in grey.*
5½ in high

This should more properly belong in the Kakiemon
section, but is included here for comparison with No. 22
showing the more usual addition of famille rose flowers.

21

22 Plate *c.* 1753
the flat rim applied with four large sprays of
prunus with three open and three half-
opened flowers and several buds, divided by
four smaller sprays, the centre and rim
painted with scattered flower-sprays in blue,
puce and yellow.
9 in diam.

22

23

24

23 A pair of large pierced circular baskets *c.* 1753

of shallow form painted with blue, puce and yellow flowers with green foliage, scattered within a pierced border of trailing flowers, the exteriors similarly decorated, the lower parts with Buddhistic emblems and flowers.
11 in diam.

Provenance:
Mrs Kathleen Tilley
Norman Wilkinson, sale Christie's, 28 April 1975, lot 5

24 A pair of oblong octagonal dishes *c.* 1753

painted in a vibrant palette with a yellow-centred pink flowering shrub issuant from blue rockwork with a bird in flight above, the wells enriched with gilt C-scrolls and foliage, within green diaper-pattern borders reserved with pink flowerheads within pale-yellow and blue cartouches.
10¾ in wide

25 Oval sauceboat *c.* 1753

with reeded loop handle and three lion-mask and paw feet, painted with flowering shrubs issuing from pierced mauve rockwork, the interior with a green trellis-pattern rim reserved with puce half-flowerheads.
9 in long

26 Oval sauceboat *c.* 1753

with a reeded loop handle and three lion-mask and large paw feet, painted in a bright famille rose palette, with puce and blue flowers with yellow centres and with foliage in opaque green, the interior with a pale-green diaper-pattern rim reserved with blue half-flowerheads, the upper terminal to the handle moulded with a shell.
7½ in long

Cf. No. 25

25

26

27

29

28

30

27 Small mug *c.* 1753
with thick loop handle, painted with an iron-red outlined pink chrysanthemum and trailing branches with foliage in two tones of green, issuing from pale-mauve pierced rockwork.
2¼ in high

28 Coffee-cup *c.* 1754
with small loop handle, painted with a pink chrysanthemum issuing from pale-blue rockwork and with trailing branches with leaves in two tones of green.

29 Saucer and Chinese coffee-cup
c. 1755
the centre painted with a figure riding a donkey within a pale-yellow ogival cartouche surrounded by flowering branches with grey-green foliage, within a pale cell and trellis-pattern rim, reserved with flowerheads, the coffee-cup in a stronger palette.

It seems quite probable that the Bow saucer was made as a replacement to complete a Chinese service of a slightly earlier date

30 Teabowl and saucer *c.* 1755
applied with three sprays of prunus with flowers, half-flowers and buds divided by famille rose flower-sprays in a wet palette, the saucer similarly decorated but with muddy-green foliage.

31 Flared teabowl and saucer *c.* 1755
painted in a pale famille rose palette with pink and blue flowers issuing from pierced blue rockwork outlined in dark-brown.

32 Bowl *c.* 1762
painted in a bright palette with pink flowers, yellow and green branches and scattered butterflies, the interior similarly painted within a chocolate line rim.
8 in diam.

It is unusual to find famille rose decoration at such a late date when the fashion had changed favouring wares with European decoration

31

32

White Wares

Bow produced large quantities of undecorated white porcelain, including many figures which will be discussed later. As with the famille rose wares in the preceding section, the influence for these was mainly Chinese, in particular the 'prunus-moulded' wares (already mentioned) which owe their origins to the wares made in the Fukien province of China towards the end of the seventeenth century.

These at first glance seem quite simple, but the variations are endless. The applied sprays are sometimes three-flowered, with three flowerheads and three buds (No. 37, which bears an incised R mark) or more elaborate with two open flowers, three half-open and three buds (No. 39, also with an incised R mark), or double prunus sprays as on the circular salt (No. 43) and the sauceboat (No. 48). These are perhaps a little later as they are rather creamy in appearance and the potting less precise; later still the moulding becomes obliterated by the glaze. This variation in colour from a grey-white to a cream colour complicates the problem of dating, as there are dated pieces of 1750 showing both variations. In general the creamier pieces seem to be later, and in this instance form is a more reliable guideline. The most frequently seen pieces belonging to this group are tea- and coffee-wares, plates and sauceboats. John Bowcock frequently mentions these wares, thus 'Mr. Fogg: 6 sprig'd handled cups and 6 cans' and again 'Mr. Fogg: a sprig'd sallad vessel, 12s: 1 pair sprig'd boats, 6s.' The egg-cup (No. 45), not of standard form, and the libation cup (No. 44), a purely Chinese form, are both great rarities, out of line with the mainstream of production.

Apart from these prunus wares but still exhibiting Fukien influence are the lizard candlesticks (No. 33); these are firmly documented in the Duesbury Account Book which suggests the flowers could be of Derby manufacture, while another indicator of early date are the mask and paw feet, similar to the sauceboats and famille rose mug already cited. The moulded festooned sauceboats (Nos. 35 and 36) are reminiscent of the Bristol and Worcester sauceboats of the 1750–52 period and also the Chelsea salts with festooned feet that belong to the triangle period, 1745–49, which again illustrate great sophistication at an early date. These, unlike the prunus wares, are purely European in concept and are derived from silver originals.

The rococo vases (No. 49) both in form and paste seem to date from the late 1750s and are more commonly found at Longton Hall or Derby. The wall-bracket (No. 50) which also appears at Derby is in a body more akin to pottery that tends to flake and chip and it could be even later than the wide period to which it is attributed.

33 A pair of white porcelain and tôle-peinte candlesticks *c.* 1750
each modelled as a central column moulded with a curled lizard on three mask and paw feet,
the drip-pans with *tôle-peinte* branches supporting white carnations and other flowers.
14 in high overall

Provenance:
David Style, Wateringbury Place, sale Christie's, 2 June 1978, lot 939

Cf. Adams (Elizabeth) and David Redstone: *Bow Porcelain*, pl. 40 for the pair in the Royal Ontario Museum, Toronto
Hurlbutt (Frank): *Bow Porcelain*, pl. 6 for a coloured example perhaps decorated by Duesbury
Tait (Hugh): 'Some Consequences of the Bow Special Exhibition, Thomas Frye and A Rival Factory in Bow', *Apollo*
1960, pt. IV, fig. I, where a Fukien original is illustrated
There is another pair in the Fitzwilliam Museum, Cambridge, *Glaisher Collection*, no. 3025-a
These are mentioned in William Duesbury's London Account Book under 8th June, 1751, 'Lisard Candle Sticks 0–0–6'

34 White and gilt vase and cover *c.* 1750
of baluster form, broadly pencilled in gold
with a Chinese river scene, with trees and
houses on river islands and with the sun and
moon painted with a face, beneath a spear-
head-pattern border, the cover with bun
finial, *incised R mark*.
9½ in high

Provenance:
Dyson Perrins Collection Worcester,
duplicate sale Sotheby's, 6 May 1969, lot 1

For the companion vase in the Ashmolean Museum
Oxford (now attributed to Bow) cf. Marshall (H. Rissik):
Coloured Worcester Porcelain, pl. 44 no 909, also another,
12 in high, in the Castle Museum, Norwich, formerly in
the Wallace Elliott Collection, sale Sotheby's, 25 May
1938, lot 244. This vase, together with the two mentioned
above, originally formed a garniture of three vases and
covers (illustrated here showing the Freeman vase on the
right), which have now been reunited by the gift of this
vase to the Ashmolean and are presently on view at the
Castle Museum, Norwich

34

34 reverse

35 White and gilt oval sauceboat *c.* 1750
with elaborate double-scroll incised handle,
the body and foot moulded with swags of
garden flowers and gilt with flower-sprays,
the interior with a gilt flower-spray and a
border of trefoil ornament, suspended from a
loop-pattern and gilt line rim.
9 in wide

Cf. No. 36
Hurlbutt (Frank): *Bow Porcelain*, pl. 5 for a similar
example but with a dragon handle
E.C.C. Exhibition Catalogue 1948, pl. 30, no. 128 for a
coloured example

35

36 Oval sauceboat *c.* 1750
with dragon handle, the body moulded with
swags of garden flowers suspended from the
scroll-moulded rim, on an oval foot moulded
with garden flowers.
7 in wide

Cf. Hurlbutt (Frank): *Bow Porcelain*, pl. 5, for a gilt
example
E.C.C. Exhibition Catalogue 1948, pl. 30, no. 127

36

41

37 38 39

40

37 Miniature ogee sugar-bowl and cover *c.* 1752
applied with three sprays of prunus with three half-flowerheads and three buds, the cover similarly decorated with button finial, *incised R mark.*
2¾ in high

Provenance:
James McG. Stewart, sale Sotheby's, 13 November 1973, lot 36

38 Bucket-shaped basket 1752–55
applied with trailing prunus sprays with rope-twist overhandle.
3 in high overall

Exhibited:
Winifred Williams: *18th Century European White Porcelain*, June 1975, fig. 14

Cf. Adams (Elizabeth) and David Redstone: *Bow Porcelain*, pl. 28

39 Ogee sugar-bowl and cover *c.* 1752
applied with three sprays of prunus with two open and three half-open flowers, divided by three flowerheads, the cover similarly decorated and with acorn finial, *incised R mark.*
5½ in high

Exhibited:
Winifred Williams: *18th Century European White Procelain*, June 1975, fig. 13

Cf. Adams (Elizabeth) and David Redstone: *Bow Porcelain*, pl. 38, for a similar example there described as a pomade pot

40 Two-handled beaker and saucer *c.* 1752
crisply applied with profusely blossomed prunus sprays, the saucer with lobed rim.

Cf. The John Bowcock Memorandum Book 'Nov. 29, 1756 ... Mr Fogg: caudle-cups, white sprig'd and saucers ...'

41 A three-shell salt *c.* 1753
the deeply moulded shells supported on pierced rockwork applied with shells and seaweed, surmounted by seaweed and a further pierced shell.
8¼ in wide

42 Shell salt *c.* 1753
of large size, the exterior deeply fluted, resting on a triangular shell-encrusted base.
5 in wide

Cf. Hurlbutt (Frank): *Bow Porcelain*, pls. 3a and 3b
Rackham (Bernard): *Schreiber Collection Catalogue*, pl. 9, no. 154
Dixon (J. L.): *English Porcelain of the 18th Century*, pl. 45

41

42

43

44

45

43 Salt *c.* 1755
the circular body applied with three double-prunus flower-sprays terminating on three mask and paw feet beneath a cream glaze.
3 in diam.

44 Oval libation cup *c.* 1755
moulded with a branch of prunus with two five-petalled flowers and a bud, the reverse with two flowers on a trailing branch, on an oval base.
3¾ in wide

Provenance:
E. H. Goulburn, sale Christie's, 8 December 1980, lot 154

Cf. Savage (George): *18th Century English Porcelain*, pl. 109A
For a Chelsea example cf. King (William): *Chelsea Porcelain*, pl. 12

45 An egg-cup *c.* 1755
the bowl with slightly everted rim applied with three sprays of prunus with two open flowers, one half-opened flower and two buds, the circular spreading foot similarly modelled.
3¼ in high

Exhibited:
Winifred Williams: *18th Century European White Porcelain*, June 1975, fig. 16

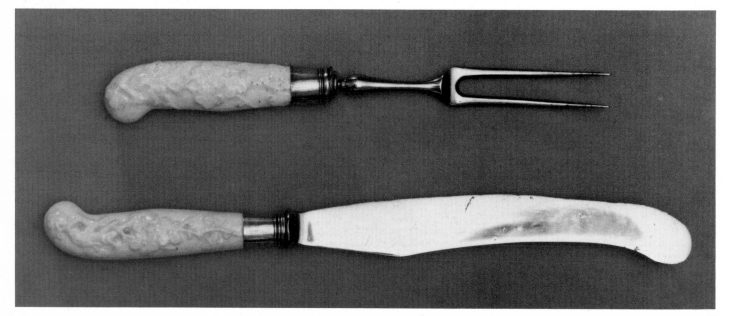

46

46 Knife-handle and fork-handle the
porcelain *c.* 1755
of pistol form, moulded with flowering
prunus with silver ferrules and fitted with a
plated two-pronged fork and curved blade.
$3\frac{1}{2}$ and 4 in long

Cf. John Ainslie: 'Knife and Fork Handles and the Bow
Collector', *The Connoisseur*, March 1953, p. 14, no IIb
The attribution of these remains uncertain and a Chelsea
origin should not be discounted

47 Vase and cover *c.* 1755
the body of ogee form applied with three
sprays of prunus each with four open flowers
and several buds on a circular spreading foot,
the cover with ball finial and similarly
decorated.
$6\frac{1}{2}$ in high

Provenance:
Anon., sale Sotheby's, 30 January 1979, lot
59

Cf. Savage (George): *18th Century English Porcelain*, pl. 41b

48 Oval sauceboat *c.* 1755
with scroll handle, elaborately applied with
heavily blossomed double prunus sprays,
terminating on three paw feet beneath a
cream glaze.
7 in wide

Cf. Adams (Elizabeth) and David Redstone: *Bow Porcelain*,
pl. 32

47

48

45

49 A pair of rococo vases 1758–60
moulded with scrolls and strapwork enriched
with shell motifs, the necks with applied
flowers on round pad bases.
4¾ in high

Provenance:
Archibald J. Corlett Willis, sale Sotheby's, 14
May 1974, lot 108

Cf. No. 136 for coloured examples forming candle-holders

49

50 Wall-bracket 1760–65
the sides deeply moulded with strapwork on
a simulated stone ground, the front with a
panel of scale-pattern between deeply incised
foliage.
5½ in high

Cf. *Untermyer Collection Catalogue*, pl. 93, fig. 290 for a
similar example formerly in the Glendenning Collection,
there attributed to Derby

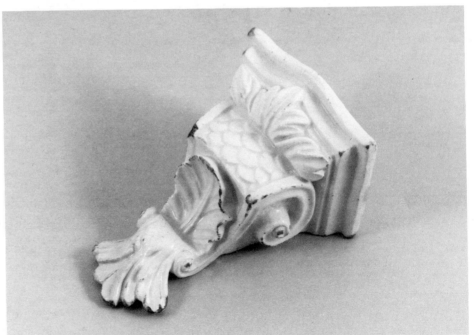

50

Wares with 'Kakiemon' Decoration

These wares owe their origins to Japanese rather than Chinese ceramics unlike the two preceding sections. More specifically, the patterns and shapes were inspired by the Kakiemon family who worked at the Arita kilns towards the end of the seventeenth and the beginning of the eighteenth centuries. The patterns are mostly of birds and beasts, in flight, perched or prowling among flowering shrubs and trees (very often the Three Friends: Pine, Prunus and Bamboo), executed in a distinctive palette of iron-red, turquoise, pale-yellow and green. Sometimes they are direct copies from Japanese originals, at others copies of a Meissen example with its inherent European peculiarities.

So prized were these Japanese wares that collections were formed by wealthy Europeans, the most notable example being Augustus the Strong, Elector of Saxony and King of Poland, who not being content to build special rooms for his collection, instructed his factory at Meissen to copy the Japanese originals and in so doing started the fashion which was soon to arrive in England.

The 'Quail Pattern' or 'Partridge Pattern' as it was then called, was clearly an enormous success and is often mentioned in John Bowcock's Memorandum Book, thus: 'Mr. Fogg: 24 octagon nappy plates, partridge pattern' May 15, Lady Stairs, partridge octagon plates' and again 'Mr. Fogg, octagon dysart partridge plate 3s 6d.'. This pattern had a long factory life and although only represented here by three pieces from about 1758–60 (Nos. 62–64) and the basket (No. 65 *c*. 1765), its production was well advanced in 1756 as shown above.

In general the Kakiemon style wares at Bow would seem to date from a little later than might be expected. The body frequently has a chalky opaque appearance. An example is the decagonal teabowl (No. 60) which if from Chelsea would date from the late raised anchor/early red anchor period and not *c*. 1755, as suggested here. There is a preponderance of octagonal forms which lend themselves to asymmetrical designs, leaving large areas in the white. However, when a purely European form is used as in No. 54, it can have the most unhappy appearance, although this same basic pattern was used to brilliant effect on the leaf-shaped dishes (Nos. 52 and 53).

There is, unlike the famille rose wares, a marked lack of tea- and coffee-wares and a large number of plates and dishes.

COLOUR PLATE III

51 Lobed oval teapot and cover *c.* 1753
painted in the Kakiemon manner with blue-branched iron-red prunus issuing from turquoise rockwork beneath an iron-red ju-i lappet border, the cover similarly decorated, the spout and handle with green and turquoise scrolls.
3¼ in high

No similar example would appear to be recorded

52 Leaf-shaped dish *c.* 1753
painted in turquoise, iron-red, grey and gold with a chrysanthemum and bamboo issuing from a banded hedge surrounded by scattered iron-red and yellow flowerheads with grey-green foliage, the reverse moulded with a trailing strawberry plant.
8¼ in wide

This type of strawberry moulding is more commonly associated with the Chelsea factory where strawberry-leaf moulded sauceboats and stands were a standard form during the 1750s
Cf. Nos. 53 and 59

53 Leaf-shaped dish *c.* 1753
similarly modelled and painted to the preceding but in a slightly less vivid palette.
7½ in wide

Cf. No. 52

54 Pierced scroll-moulded oval centrepiece *c.* 1753
the centre painted with a bird in flight above prunus and bamboo issuing from banded hedges, surrounded by gilt scroll work and vase cartouches painted with black river landscapes, divided by prunus and bamboo issuing from banded hedges and scattered iron-red flowerheads with gilt centres, within a shaped gilt line rim, the underside similarly painted with trailing branches and blue and iron-red yellow-centred flowerheads, on a similarly painted shaped oval foot.
13¾ in long

No similar example would appear to be recorded

52

53

54

55

56

57

55 Tapering vase *c.* 1755
with short flared neck and shaped domed
foot, painted with an Oriental figure wearing
a turquoise kimono and with a flowering
shrub issuing from two banded hedges, the
reverse with loosely scattered flower-sprays,
beneath an iron-red scroll and loop-pattern
rim.

8½ in high

Cf. *E.C.C. Commemorative Exhibition Catalogue 1977*, no. 131
for a vase of similar form

56 Square dish *c.* 1755
painted in underglaze-blue, overglaze
turquoise, iron-red and pale-yellow with a
fighting cock and a hen within a double-line
square cartouche, the border with two
dragons and flowering shrubs among iron-
red, gilt, pale-yellow and green cloud-scrolls
within a chocolate line rim, the reverse with
four stylised trailing branches, *blue square seal
mark within a single circle.*

5 in wide

Exhibited:
Winifred Williams: *The Kakiemon Influence on
European Porcelain*, 1974, no. 41

Cf. Adams (Elizabeth) and David Redstone: *Bow Porcelain*,
col. pl. F

57 Octagonal dish *c.* 1755
after an Arita original painted with
alternating panels of emblems and flowers
with iron-red panels with white whorl-
pattern, the border similarly decorated.
8 in wide

Cf. Adams (Elizabeth) and David Redstone: *Bow Porcelain*,
pl. 48

58 Octagonal deep bowl *c.* 1755
painted with an Oriental lady wearing a
turquoise kimono with gilt flowers and with
an iron-red belt, the reverse with flowering
shrubs issuing from a banded hedge, the
interior with a man flying a kite and a
Buddhistic lion, within a border of iron-red,
turquoise and green scrolling foliage and
flowers.
7¼ in wide

58

59

60

59 Fluted beaker 1753–55
painted in iron-red and black with prunus
and bamboo issuing from a banded hedge,
the reverse with a pale-yellow phoenix with
an iron-red tail in flight, *incised arrow and
annulet mark.*
2¼ in high

60 Decagonal teabowl *c.* 1755
painted with The Lady in the Pavilion
Pattern in turquoise, blue and iron-red
lightly enriched in gilding beneath a
chocolate rim, the interior with a flowerhead
with iron-red foliage.

Cf. Mallett (John): 'A Chelsea Talk', *E.C.C. Transactions*,
vol. 6, pt. 1, pl. 26, where both a Japanese original and a
Bow example are illustrated
A decagonal teabowl and a saucer of this pattern were
sold at Christie's, 15 December 1975, lot 130
Perhaps a replacement for a Chelsea service of slightly
earlier date

61 A pair of bottles c. 1755

the spherical bodies with tall cylindrical necks, painted in lemon-yellow, turquoise, green, iron-red and gilding with an exotic bird perched on a flowering shrub, flanked by further flowering shrubs, the neck with iron-red scrolling foliage and gilt flowers. 7½ in high

Provenance:
James McG. Stewart, sale Sotheby's, 13 November 1973, lot 52

Literature:
Godden (Geoffrey): *Oriental Export Market Porcelain*, pl. 250

Cf. *E.C.C. Transactions*, vol. 1, pl. XIV

COLOUR PLATE IV
62 Cylindrical ink-pot c. 1760

painted with The Quail Pattern, the shoulder pierced with four holes for pens and with tight iron-red scrolls with gilt quatrefoil flowerheads. 3½ in diam.

Provenance:
Anon., sale Sotheby's, 16 June 1981, lot 129

Ink-pots of this date are most unusual, the well-documented New Canton ink-pots date from a period some ten years earlier. All six recorded examples being inscribed and dated, four with the date 1750, one with the date 1751 and another dated 1752, which may be seen in the following collections:
(a) 'MADE AT NEW CANTON 1750', a blue and white example – Colchester Museum, cf. Watney (Bernard) *English Blue and White Porcelain of the 18th Century*, pl. 2A
(b) 'MADE AT NEW CANTON 1750', enamelled with prunus and banded hedges – British Museum, cf. Hurlbutt (Frank): *Bow Porcelain*, pl. 2A
(c) 'MADE AT NEW CANTON 1750', similarly painted to the preceding – The Salisbury & South Wiltshire Museum, cf. Adams (Elizabeth) and David Redstone: *Bow Porcelain*, colour pl. B
(d) 'MADE AT NEW CANTON 1750', similarly painted to the preceding – Fitzwilliam Museum, Cambridge, Lord and Lady Fisher's Collection (C8-1951)
(e) 'MADE AT NEW CANTON 1751', similarly painted to the preceding – Victoria & Albert Museum, cf. Hurlbutt (Frank): *op cit.*, pl. 2B
(f) 'EDWARD VERNON ESQR., JULY 1752', a blue and white example painted with figures among pagodas, rockwork and shrubs – Brighton Art Gallery Museum, cf. Watney (Bernard): *op. cit.* pl. 3D

61

62

63 Tapering coffee-pot and shallow cover *c.* 1758
with steeply curving spout and loop handle with flat thumb-piece painted with The Quail Pattern, the cover with closed pink rosebud finial with green foliage and blue flower-head terminals.
9 in high

Provenance:
Anon., sale Phillips, 27 September 1978, lot 190

For a similarly painted chocolate-pot, of earlier date, see the Frank Arnold sale Sotheby's, 12 November 1963, lot 23

63

64 Shell-moulded oval dish *c.* 1760
the interior painted with The Quail Pattern
within a border of iron-red scrolling foliage
and gilt flowerheads, the exterior crisply
modelled as a shell, the rim enriched in pink,
on three seaweed and shell-encrusted
rockwork feet.
6½ in wide

Provenance:
Miss Joan Greaves, sale Sotheby's, 1 July
1975, lot 95

64

65 Pierced flared circular basket *c.* 1765
the interior painted with The Quail Pattern
with scattered iron-red flowers, the exterior
left in the white and with applied
flowerheads at the intersections.
8½ in diam.

Provenance:
H. Beven Collection
Anon., sale Phillips, 26 March 1980, lot 151

Cf. Hobson (R. L.): *Catalogue of English Porcelain in the
British Museum*, p. 19, fig. 14
Adams (Elizabeth) and David Redstone: *Bow Porcelain*, pl.
55 for an example of earlier date
Also No. 111 for a blue and white example of similar form

65

Wares with Underglaze-blue Decoration

Unlike Chelsea who produced less than a dozen pieces of blue and white, Bow made enormous quantities. Indeed their blue and white production may be seen as a yardstick for the rest of their output and largely explains their commercial success. Blue and white was produced from the beginning through to the early 1770s, these limits being illustrated by the dated NEW CANTON ink-pot in Colchester Museum and the WILLIAM AND ELIZABETH MARTIN bowl in the British Museum, both of 1750, and the IOSEPH & MARGRET PENNYFEATHER mug in the Victoria & Albert Museum and the ROBERT CROWTHER plate in the British Museum, both of 1770.

The earliest wares are mostly in a bright, vivid blue peculiar to Bow. Frequently, though not always, these have a thick, lardy glaze, sometimes as though they had been glazed twice, and they are frequently subject to crazing. These I believe to be contemporary with the coloured 'drab' wares already mentioned. The plate (No. 66) is peculiar in the way in which the painter has used large areas of shaded wash, while the 'telegraph pole' trees are a recurrent motif which appears on later wares. To complicate the issue, the plate (No. 67) which is also painted in this bright 'early' blue is also recorded in the grey-blue similar to the MARTIN bowl. Thus either these two tones of blue are contemporary and produced side by side or, as is implied here, the grey-blue wares may be of the slightly later date of 1750 to about 1754 (see the dated bowl No. 85).

The Imari type wares belong on the whole to the early bright-blue group and it is interesting to note that the tureen and cover (No. 70) bears an incised nick mark closely linking it to the other tureen (No. 75) which is painted in a sooty grey-blue associated with the incised R marked wares. The exceptions here are the Imari plates (No. 74) painted in a grey-blue yet having a thick glaze.

The two heart-shaped sweetmeat-dishes (Nos. 81 and 82) are interesting. Although one is Chinese, the original source may have been either Meissen or English delftware. Here we see the beginnings of stock patterns. The early bright-blue has gone as has the grey-blue to make way for a dull royal-blue which gets progressively darker as the wares get later in date. The bottle (No. 89) based on an early pattern, is here seen in a later version with elaborate diaper borders. The 'Golfer and Caddy Pattern' octagonal plate (No. 88) is another standard pattern which does not appear much before 1758 and is sometimes found with painters' numerals. This blue frequently has a rather dried out, almost sugary look as though it had been absorbed by the body of the object, and the glaze often has a bluish tinge from the addition of cobalt.

The baluster coffee-pot (No. 95) has its counterpart at Worcester in the herring-bone moulded examples, normally dating from 1758–62. This attempt by Bow to copy Worcester patterns can be seen again with the cream-jug (No. 102) showing the 'Mansfield Pattern' and a large number of powder-blue wares which generally seem to have been previously dated too early on the evidence of the Bowcock bowl of 1759. The powder-blue vase and cover (No. 96) reveals an interesting use of late Imari style which, as has been shown, is normally associated with the early 1750s, the influence on this occasion being Chinese rather than Japanese.

Towards the end of the 1760s the wares became more like pottery in appearance and were slavishly painted. The forms were copied from other factories, for example No. 113 from Worcester, No. 112 from Derby and they may easily be of later date than that ascribed to them here. If Bow did continue producing blue and white well into the 1770s, the leaf-dishes (No. 116) seem the most probable candidates.

66 Plate 1749–52
boldly painted in a bright tone of blue with a house and a pine tree in the foreground, a stretch of water beyond with two islands with stylised trees, within a circular ogival cartouche, the border with trellis-pattern reserved with trailing flowers, all beneath a thick glaze.
9 in diam.

Provenance:
Anon., sale Sotheby's, 26 November 1974, lot 154

Cf. *E.C.C. Exhibition Catalogue, 1948*, pl. 34, no. 153
Adams (Elizabeth) and David Redstone: *Bow Porcelain*, pl. 18 and another from the Bradley Collection sold at Christie's, 12 October 1981, lot 19

66

67 Plate 1749–52

painted in a bright tone of blue with a scroll
containing a flowering shrub issuing from
pierced rockwork by a fence flanked by
Buddhist emblems and trailing flowers above
and below, within a diamond-pattern and
foliage rim, reserved with four panels of
flowerheads, the reverse with three trailing
branches, beneath a thick glaze.
8¾ in diam.

Cf. *E.C.C. Exhibition Catalogue, 1948*, pl. 34, no. 154 for the
Toppin example
Klaber & Klaber: *Oriental Influences on European Porcelain*,
no. 51A
Adams (Elizabeth) and David Redstone: *Bow Porcelain*,
pl. 19 and another from the Bradley Collection sold at
Christie's, 12 October 1981, lot 21
Taken directly from the Chinese and also copied on
English delftware

67

**68 A pair of double-lipped two-handled
sauceboats** 1749–52

with small scroll handles, painted in the
Imari palette in underglaze-blue, overglaze
iron-red and gilding with trailing flowering
branches, the interior rim with diaper-pattern
reserved with panels of iron-red flowerheads,
beneath a thick glaze.
7¼ in long

68

69 A pair of baluster finger-bowls
1749–52
painted in the Imari palette in underglaze-blue and overglaze iron-red and gilding with trailing flowering branches issuing from pierced blue rockwork, the interior with iron-red scrolls suspended from a blue and gilt loop-pattern rim, *blue B marks.*
3½ in diam.
Provenance:
Anon., sale Sotheby's, 20 November 1979, lots 80 and 81

70 Shallow circular tureen and domed cover 1749–52
the rope-twist handles with female mask and scroll terminals, painted in the Imari palette with flowering shrubs issuing from blue rockwork within elaborate iron-red diaper-pattern rims reserved with panels of flowerheads, the lower rim painted as radiating lappets with flowerheads on a blue ground, *incised nick mark.*
9½ in diam.

71 Baluster mug 1749–52
with grooved loop handle, painted in the Imari palette in underglaze-blue and overglaze iron-red and gilding with flowering shrubs issuing from pierced blue rockwork beneath a diaper-pattern and flowerhead rim, *large incised X mark.*
6 in high

Cf. Nos. 72 and 73

72 Baluster mug 1749–52
painted in the Imari palette with flowering shrubs issuing from pierced rockwork, a gap in the rockwork inscribed 'IM' in red, the lower border with alternating blue panels with gilt trellis-pattern and iron-red flowers, *incised line mark.*
3¼ in high

Provenance:
Anon., sale Sotheby's, 20 October 1981, lot 119

73 Baluster mug *c.* 1752
painted in the Imari palette with underglaze-blue flowering shrubs issuing from pierced rockwork and enriched in iron-red and gilding beneath a diaper-pattern rim reserved with flowerheads.
3½ in high

71

72

73

74 A pair of plates *c.* 1752
painted in the Imari palette in a pale
underglaze-blue and enriched in iron-red and
gilding, with a quatrefoil jardinière of
flowers, the blue wells with gilt trailing
foliage within a border of trailing flowering
plants and gilt tightly scrolling foliage
enriched in iron-red, beneath a thick glaze.
9 in diam.

Provenance:
Mrs. O. J. Fortescue

Anon., sale Christie's, 20 June 1977, lot 135

Taken directly from a Japanese original

75 Circular tureen and domed cover

c. 1750

the flat loop handles with mask terminals, painted with elaborate pagodas with striped roofs among hatch-pattern rockwork and willow, pine and flowering shrubs, two Orientals holding parasols on a river island with a bird in flight above, within a hatch-pattern border, the cover with lion finial with curling mane, his left forepaw resting on a tree-stump, *incised line mark.*

$11\frac{1}{2}$ in wide

Provenance:

Anon., sale Christie's, 17 November 1975, lot 107

The finial appears as a figure on its own, cf. Rackham (Bernard): *Schreiber Collection Catalogue*, pl. 9, no. 146. There is a similar tureen but with Kakiemon decoration in the National Museum, Dublin (1040–1909)

76 Tapering oviform vase *c.* 1750

painted in a soft blue with a trailing flowering shrub issuing from shaded pierced rockwork beneath an elaborate half-flowerhead-pattern border enriched with diaper-pattern, suspending swags of flowers and foliage, the lower rim with half-flowerheads and half-diamond-shaped medallions, *incised R mark.*

$6\frac{1}{2}$ in high

Provenance:

Anon., sale Sotheby's, 22 November 1977, lot 88

Cf. Watney (Bernard): *English Blue and White Porcelain of the 18th Century*, pl. 4A

77 Shallow cyclindrical butter-tub and cover *c.* 1750

with two D-shaped lug handles, the exterior painted with trailing flowering branches in a bright blue with hatched foliage and flowers, the cover similarly painted and with loop handle.

$5\frac{1}{4}$ in diam.

Provenance:

Dr John Ainslie, sale Sotheby's, 7 March 1961, lot 57

Anon., sale Sotheby's, 6 May 1975, lot 182

Literature:

Watney (Bernard): *English Blue and White Porcelain of the 18th Century*, pl. 7C

76

77

78

79

78 Coffee-cup 1752–54
with moulded double handle painted in a
pale blue with a house, two pagodas,
rockwork and shrubs by a tent-shaped fence,
the interior with a diaper-pattern and
flowerhead border.

79 Flared teabowl 1752–54
painted in a pale grey-blue with a trailing
flowering branch issuing from pierced
rockwork between line rims, the interior with
a double line rim.

80 Bowl 1752–54
painted in a bright tone of blue with an
Oriental standing on a wooded river island
with another figure in a boat in the distance,
the reverse with flowering shrubs and
bamboo issuing from pierced rockwork, *blue
H mark*.
7 in diam.

80

81 Heart-shaped sweetmeat-dish *c.* 1753
painted in a bright blue with figures on a
quay with a boat in the foreground within an
ogival cartouche, *four character mock Oriental
mark.*

5 in wide

Literature:
Klaber & Klaber: *Oriental Influences on
European Porcelain*, pls. 58 and 58A

Cf. Watney (Bernard): *English Blue and White Porcelain of
the 18th Century*, pl. 10A(2)

**82 Chinese heart-shaped sweetmeat-
dish** *c.* 1750
similarly painted to the preceding, Qianlong.
5 in wide

Cf. footnote to the preceding item, No. 81

83 Lobed oval dish *c.* 1754
painted with a harbour scene with a boat at
sail and two rowing boats among
waterweeds, by a quay with further boats in
the distance with four outlined clouds above
within a blue wave-pattern border.
9½ in long

Cf. Watney (Bernard): *English Blue and White Porcelain of
the 18th Century*, pl. 10A(2) for a similarly painted pickle-
tray

84 detail

84

85 underside

85

84 Baluster mug *c. 1754*

with grooved loop handle painted in a bright
blue with a figure crossing a bridge from one
island with a willow tree on pierced rockwork
to another with a figure in a sentry box,
two further figures in the distance beneath a
diaper-pattern rim reserved with half-
flowerheads, the interior inscribed '3 Poice'
with a semi-circular mark above, *mock
Oriental marks and painter's mark H beneath the
handle.*
3½ in high

Provenance:
Anon., sale Sotheby's, 24 October 1978, lot
64

85 Dated bowl 1754

the exterior with a border of honeycomb-
pattern reserved with panels of flowerheads
and foliage, the lower part with scrolls the
base with the date 1754 within a double
circle, the interior with a flowerhead within a
double circle.
4¾ in diam.

Provenance:
Anon., sale Phillips, 5 June 1974, lot 156

Literature:
Adams (Elizabeth) and David Redstone: *Bow
Porcelain*, pl. 83

86 Miniature teabowl and saucer

c. 1758
painted in a pale-blue with trailing vine and
two bunches of grapes within a line rim.

Cf. Adams (Elizabeth) and David Redstone: *Bow Porcelain*,
pl. 102

87 Circular stand 1756–58

after a Chinese original, painted with an
ogival cartouche of radiating panels of figures
and flowering shrubs, surrounded by
flowering plants within a border of stylised
four-petalled flowerheads, within a lobed rim.
6 in diam.

It seems most likely that this is a stand for a circular
butter-tub

86

87

65

88 Octagonal plate *c.* 1758
painted in two tones of blue with The Golfer
and Caddy Pattern beneath a precipice with
a horizontal branch above, within a waved
blue rim, *painter's numeral 5.*
7 in diam.

Cf. Hurlbutt (Frank): *Bow Porcelain*, pl. 8A for a saucer
E.C.C. Exhibition Catalogue, 1948, pl. 32, no. 155 for another
plate
Watney. (Bernard): *English Blue and White Porcelain of the
18th Century*, pl. 10C(I) for a pickle-dish

89 Bottle 1756–60
the spherical body with a slender garlic neck
painted with a flower and enormous leaf
surrounded by dots and enriched with hatch-
pattern, with two bamboo trees in the
background beneath the shoulder with a
band of diaper-pattern reserved with four
blue quatrefoil cartouches of foliage, the neck
with stylised scrolls, foliage and stiff leaves,
the bulbous upper part with diaper-pattern
beneath a tight scroll-pattern rim, *painter's
numeral 59 and incised CA mark.*
9½ in high

Literature:

Klaber & Klaber: *Oriental Influences on
European Porcelain*, no 50A

88

90

90 Knife-handle *c.* 1754

of moulded pistol form with scrolls and swags of flowers enriched in blue and with added flower-sprays, the lower part with a band of buds.

4 in long

Provenance:
The Marquess of Lansdowne, sale Sotheby's, 20 December 1972, part lot 12

91 A pair of large knife-handles *c.* 1758

of pistol form, painted with hatched foliage, C-scrolls and stylised strapwork, the upper parts with stylised bell-shaped flowerheads divided by cell-pattern panels.

5 in long

Provenance:
The Marquess of Lansdowne, sale Sotheby's, 20 December 1972, part lot 12

92 Knife-handle and fork-handle
1754–58

painted in a bright blue with hatched foliage, stylised strapwork and lambrequins, the upper parts with bell flowers suspended from a border of cell-pattern, fitted with a steel three-pronged fork and curved blade attached with silver ferrules.

2¼ in and 3½ in long

93 Two knife-handles and two fork-handles *c.* 1758

of pistol form, each painted with a cornucopia, scrolls and stylised foliage, the fork in a darker blue, fitted with steel two-pronged forks and curved blades.

3½ in and 4 in long

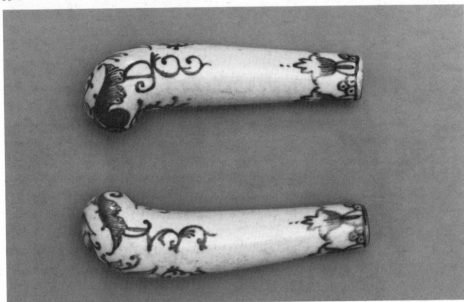

91

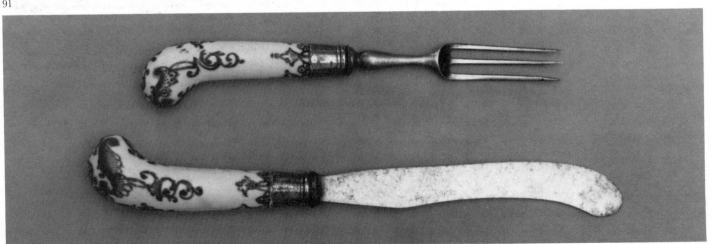

92

94

94 Piggin-spoon *c.* 1760

the hemispherical bowl with a shallowly
fluted exterior painted with flower-sprays and
foliage, the interior with a band
of flowerheads and foliage, the stem formed of
two sections, the underside with a spur.
3½ in long

**95 Baluster coffee-pot and domed
cover** 1760–62

with shaped scroll handle and scroll-moulded
curved spout, the body with overlapping
foliage moulding reserved with two scroll-
moulded cartouches painted with a flower-
spray, butterflies and insects, the top and rim
to the cover painted with flowerheads and
tightly scrolling foliage, *mock Oriental mark.*
10 in high

Provenance:
Dr John Ainslie, sale Sotheby's, 7 March
1961, lot 155
Anon., sale Phillips, 7 November 1979, lot
170

95

96 Powder-blue baluster vase and domed cover *c.* 1760

painted in the Imari palette in underglaze-blue, overglaze iron-red and gilding, with chrysanthemum and other flower-sprays within vase-shaped, circular and quatrefoil cartouches, the ground lightly gilt with foliage beneath a thick glaze.

11½ in high

Provenance:
Captain Derek Cooper RN, sale Sotheby's, 7 October 1969, lot 46
Anon., sale Christie's, 3 February 1975, lot 143
Literature:
Adams (Elizabeth) and David Redstone: *Bow Porcelain*, pl. 91

96

97

98

97 Baluster mug 1760–62
the grooved strap handle with heart-shaped
terminal, the border with white flowerheads
on a hatch-pattern ground reserved with
three ju-i lappets, the lower part with a band
of cell-pattern, the circular spreading foot
with loop and dot-pattern.
5 in high

Cf. Watney (Bernard): *English Blue and White Porcelain of
the 18th Century*, pl. 14D for a mug of similar type inscribed
'Mrs Ann Ambler 1762' now in the National Museum of
Wales, Cardiff

98 Chamber-candlestick *c.* 1760
of triangular leaf-moulded form with loop
handle and tulip-shaped nozzle, painted with
bouquets of garden flowers within a *feuille-de-
choux* rim.
6¼ in wide

Provenance:
Anon., sale Sotheby's, 23 October 1979, lot
198 and there attributed to Derby

Cf. Savage (George): *Porcelain Through the Ages*, p. 57, pl. A
Adams (Elizabeth) and David Redstone: *Bow Porcelain*,
col. pl. N

99 Bowl 1762–65
painted in a bright blue with a dragon
pursuing a flaming pearl among cloud scrolls
extending over the rim to the exterior
beneath a bluish glaze.
8 in diam.

99

100 Large globular teapot and cover
c. 1762
with short curved spout and loop handle,
painted in a blurred deep-blue with a dragon
pursuing the flaming pearl among cloud
scrolls, the cover similarly decorated and
with ball finial.
7 in high

Provenance:
Anon., sale Phillips, 2 May 1979, lot 145

101 **Miniature teapot and cover** 1762–65
with short spout and loop handle painted
with trailing flowers with hatched foliage and
petals, beneath a loop and line rim, the cover
with similar painting.
3¼ in high

Provenance:
Anon., sale Sotheby's, 30 January 1979,
lot 53

102 **Baluster cream-jug** 1762–65
with small loop handle, loosely painted with
trailing peony beneath a lambrequin-pattern
rim.
2¾ in high

103 **Powder-blue egg-cup** 1762–65
the rim with two half-ogival panels of flowers
divided by three circular panels of
flowerheads on a circular spreading foot with
two further circular panels, *mock Oriental
mark*.
2½ in high

Provenance:
Anon., sale Sotheby's, 22 November 1977, lot
89

Cf. Watney (Bernard): *Blue and White Porcelain of the 18th
Century*, pl. 13A

104 **Powder-blue globular teapot and
cover** 1762–65
with curved spout and loop handle, painted
with two fan-shaped cartouches containing a
house on a river island flanked by five trees
with a boulder in the foreground and with
another house with a willow tree and other
shrubs, a circular cartouche with a flower-
spray above and below the spout, the cover
similarly decorated with button finial.
6 in high

Provenance:
Dr John Ainslie, sale Sotheby's, 7 March
1961, part lot 153
Anon., sale Phillips, 7 November 1979, lot
169

105 **The bowl from a powder-blue oval
ladle** the porcelain *c.* 1765
the centre painted with a pagoda among
rockwork on a wooded river island within a
lobed powder-blue border, the underside in
powder-blue, the handle mounted in silver,
the silver Sheffield, 1947.
4½ in long overall

101

102

103

104

105

107 Oval cream-boat *c.* 1765
moulded with panels of sheep, lambs and
cows divided by panels of basketweave-
pattern, the interior with trailing flowers
beneath a cell-pattern border.
4¾ in long

Provenance:
Gilbert Bradley, sale Christie's, 12 October
1981, lot 60, there catalogued as probably
Bow

<sub>Although Lowestoft examples of this mould are recorded,
cf. Watney (Bernard): *English Blue and White Porcelain of the
18th Century*, pl. 79B, no other Bow example has been
recorded</sub>

108 Oval potted-meat dish *c.* 1765
boldly painted in tones of blue with an
elaborate house and a pagoda among
rockwork and trees, the reverse with a figure
fishing from an arched bridge with hills in
the distance and flanked by a willow tree, the
interior with a flower-spray beneath a scroll
and line-pattern rim.
4½ in wide

Provenance:
Dr John Ainslie, sale Sotheby's, 7 March
1961, part lot 59
Anon., sale Christie's, 9 February 1981, lot
151

109 Oval butter-tub and cover *c.* 1765
with moulded scroll lug handles, the exterior
painted with trailing flowers with hatched
foliage, the cover similarly painted and with
bud finial.
4 in wide

Provenance:
Dr John Ainslie, sale Sotheby's, 7 March
1961, part lot 59
Anon., sale Christie's, 9 February 1981, lot
151

106

106 Powder-blue circular dish *c.* 1765
the centre with a circular medallion of a
pagoda on a wooded river island with a
further island to the left and a sampan
between, surrounded by four fan-shaped and
four circular medallions of river islands and
flower-sprays, *mock Oriental character mark*.
12½ in diam.

Provenance:
W. L. Little

Exhibited:
E.C.C. Exhibition Catalogue, 1948, pl. 32, no.
159

<sub>For this type of decoration cf. Watney (Bernard): *English
Blue and White Porcelain of the 18th Century*, pp. 13, 14, 21
and pls. 12 and 13A</sub>

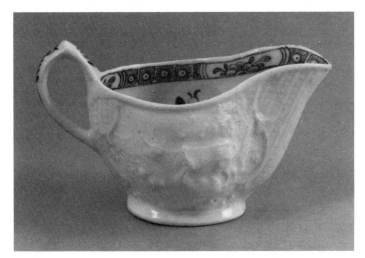

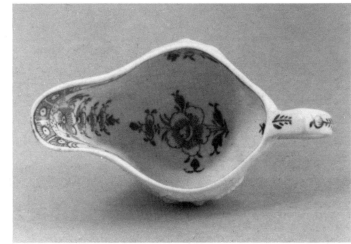

107

107 interior

108

109

110 Lobed oval dish *c.* 1765
moulded with two branches of trailing vine
coloured in tones of blue with darker veins
and with scattered insects and a bird within
a moulded C-scroll rim, *four character mock
Oriental mark*.
11¾ in wide

111 Pierced flared circular basket

c. 1765

the interior painted with trailing flower-sprays, the centre with a daisy, a spray of flowers and scattered flower-sprays within a lobed rim with flowerheads and foliage, the exterior painted with blue flowerheads at the intersections, the footrim with vertical gadrooning.

8½ in diam.

Cf. No. 65 for a Quail Pattern basket of similar form

111

112 Quatrefoil tureen, cover and ladle 1765–70

painted with a pagoda among trees divided by two panels of a flowering plant and two birds in flight, the cover with apple and foliage finial, within cell-pattern borders, the spoon with an oval bowl and curved handle, painted with flowers.

6½ in long

Cf. Watney (Bernard): *English Blue and White Porcelain of the 18th Century*, pl. 18C for a similar example formerly in the Ainslie Collection. The form and pattern are also recorded at Derby

112

113

114

115

113 Geranium leaf-moulded butter-boat 1765–70
with small loop handle, the interior painted
with five flower-sprays with deep blue foliage,
within a blue *feuille-de-choux* rim.
2¾ in wide

After a Worcester model

114 Leaf-shaped pickle-dish 1765–70
painted with a bunch of grapes resting on a
veined leaf within a shaped *feuille-de-choux*
rim, the underside with raised veins.
3½ in wide

115 Shell salt 1765–70
the interior boldly painted with a bunch of
grapes resting on a veined vine-leaf within a
feuille-de-choux rim, the exterior with deep
fluting, on three cone feet.
4½ in wide

116 Four leaf-shaped dishes *c.* 1770
boldly painted in tones of blue with a vine-
leaf and two bunches of grapes within a
shaped *feuille-de-choux* rim, *four character mock
Oriental marks.*
10¼ in wide

Cf. *E.C.C. Exhibition Catalogue, 1948*, pl. 33, no. 158, for a
similar example

116

Transfer-printed Wares

One of the most fortuitous inventions for the porcelain manufacturer was the advent of transfer printing and its use as applied to ceramics. It was a cheap and commercially viable method of decorating porcelain and pottery but one in which unfortunately Bow failed to achieve a great success. This lack of success probably contributed to the factory's eventual demise.

There are no counterparts at Bow to the early overglaze transfers in black of about 1753, known as 'smoky primitives' at Worcester and associated with Boitard and Hancock. Dr Bernard Watney in his paper 'Notes on Bow Transfer-Printing' (*E.C.C. Transactions*, vol. 8, pt. 2, pp. 213–23) has clearly shown the five main groups into which the Bow transfers belong. *Group A*, 1754–56, have floral borders similar to the Target flower-pot, here illustrated by No. 117. *Group B*, 1754–57 have a trefoil loop border as shown by the Aeneas and Anchises plate (No. 118), the prints often have closer links with Worcester. *Group C*, 1757–60, have prints in purple, red, lilac and black with simple line rims (Nos. 119–121), frequently using poor, very worn copper plates, as in the Anti-Gallican Society plate (No. 121). *Group D*, 1760s, have coloured-in outline prints; although rather unimaginative and not aesthetically pleasing, they were perhaps the most commercially successful range of the transfer output, and are here represented by Nos. 123–125. *Group E*, underglaze-blue prints, are here represented by a single plate (No. 122).

117

119 Octagonal shallow soup-plate
1756–58
transfer-printed in purple after Robert Hancock with 'L'Amour', the border with three houses in landscape vignettes within a purple line rim.
9 in diam.

Provenance:
Cyril Cook
Dr John Ainslie
G. W. Capell, sale Sotheby's, 16 February 1965, lot 23
Sir William Mullens, sale Sotheby's, 22 February 1977, lot 125

Cf. Adams (Elizabeth) and David Redstone: *Bow Porcelain*, col. pl. 1
Also No. 117

120 Saucer-dish *c.* 1760
with slightly everted rim, transfer-printed after Robert Hancock in pale-purple, the central print with a cockerel, two hens and four chicks beneath a tree with mountains in the distance surrounded by three further prints of a pheasant, grouse, a cockerel and a hen with two chicks in small landscape vignettes within a dark-chocolate rim.
8 in diam.

Cf. Cook (Cyril): *The Life and Work of Robert Hancock*, no. 23
H. W. Hughes: 'Authorship of Some Designs on Porcelain and Enamel and Robert Hancock's Connection with Battersea and Bow', *E.C.C. Transactions*, vol. 1, no. 3, pl. XL
Watney (Bernard): 'Notes on Bow Transfer-Printing', *E.C.C. Transactions*, vol. 8, pt. 2, pl. 170C

121 Plate *c.* 1760
the centre transfer-printed in puce with the badge of the Anti-Gallican Society, the shield with St George flanked by a lion rampant and an eagle of the Holy Roman Empire with Britannia above, seated among flags and military trophies and the motto 'For Our Country' below, the border with three landscape vignettes.
9 in diam.

Provenance:
Cyril Cook, no. 230
Anon., sale Phillips, 18 June 1980, lot 128

Cf. Cook (Cyril): *The Life and Work of Robert Hancock*, supplement item 25

117 Saucer-dish 1754–56
with slightly flared rim, the centre transfer-printed in iron-red with 'L'Amour', the border with puce, yellow, iron-red and blue flowerheads and iron-red foliage.
8 in diam.

Provenance:
Dr John Ainslie, sale Sotheby's, 7 March 1961, lot 124
Sir William Mullens, sale Sotheby's, 22 February 1977, lot 122

Literature:
Adams (Elizabeth) and David Redstone: *Bow Porcelain*, pl. 72

Cf. Cook (Cyril): *The Life and Work of Robert Hancock*, item 2, figs 1, 2 and 3
Also No. 119

118 Saucer-dish 1754–57
transfer-printed in iron-red with Aeneas and Anchises fleeing from the burning city of Troy within a C-scroll and ribbon cartouche, the border with loop and trefoil motifs in iron-red.
7¾ in diam.

Provenance:
G. W. Capell, sale Sotheby's, 16 February 1965, lot 21
Sir William Mullens, sale Sotheby's, 22 February 1977, lot 128

Cf. Cook (Cyril): *The Life and Work of Robert Hancock*, item 1
Watney (Bernard): *E.C.C. Transactions*, vol. 9, pt. 3, pl. 175, fig. A
Rackham (Bernard): *Schreiber Collection Catalogue*, pl. 13, no. 71
Taken from a design by Gravelot

118

119

120

121

122

122 Plate 1762–65
transfer-printed in underglaze-blue with three
figures and two oxen beneath rockwork and
beside a tree, the border with five flower-
sprays.
8 in diam.

Provenance:
Dr John Ainslie, sale Sotheby's, 7 March
1961, lot 120
Sir William Mullens, sale Sotheby's, 22
February 1977, lot 124

123 Lobed oval dish *c.* 1765
outline-printed in black and coloured in blue,
turquoise, yellow, puce and tones of green
with three figures seated and standing by a
table beneath a pine tree and among shrubs
within a shaped chocolate rim, *blue three dot
mark.*
8¼ in long

Cf. No. 125 for the same transfer

124 Tapering oviform vase 1765–68
with flared neck, outline-printed in black and
coloured in green, blue, yellow and puce
with Oriental figures seated and standing by
a tree among furniture and vases, beneath a
chocolate line rim.
9 in high

125 Oviform vase 1765–68
outline-printed in black and coloured in
green, puce, blue, mauve and yellow with
Oriental figures among furniture and vases
beneath trees and shrubs, beneath a
chocolate line rim, on a circular spreading
foot.
7 in high

Cf. Nos. 123 and 124 for the same transfers

123

124

125

Wares with European Decoration

The Oriental styles of Kakiemon and famille rose painting were soon rejected by the European decorator, who was quick to see a chance for commercial success. This is a pattern which can be seen throughout the Continent. For example at Meissen, Herold's chinoiseries gave way to bouquets and naturalistic flower painting and insects in the manner of Klinger. There was a craze for attaining perfection in the mimicry of nature. This did not apply simply to the way in which objects were painted but also to their form. The move away from Oriental mannerism occurred at Meissen in the early 1740s and was to reach England in the early 1750s at Chelsea. By the middle of the decade the change was well established.

The passion for the natural is epitomised in the botanical dish (No. 129), a form and style more commonly associated with Chelsea and the so-called 'Hans Sloane' plates. Such patterns were generally copied from botanical prints but may have been taken directly from nature at one of the botanic gardens established at the time. The palette here is particularly dry and possesses a patchy quality which is especially noticeable on the stems in the close-up photograph. This watered-down effect of the enamel is a peculiar quality of some Bow porcelain.

The flower painting may be divided into several closely connected yet distinct types:
(1) a pale delicate style with loose bouquets, trailing flowers and scattered insects (Nos. 132 and 133)
(2) an altogether heavier style with a fondness for pink and yellow roses, the latter heavily shaded in black with foliage in a grey-green (No. 135)
(3) loose bouquets in a pale patchy palette, previously mentioned, with cotton stems, a fondness again for pink roses and an open chrysanthemum (Nos. 137, 144 and 149)
(4) a style very close to Chelsea painting, perhaps taken from Meissen, very precise and giving an overall impression of fine brushwork, especially noticable on the vase and the Handel clock-case (Nos. 138 and 139).
(5) About 1759–60, the palette changes to a type more commonly associated with the factory, altogether stronger with a rich yellow, puce and turquoise. This major group which in effect is a culmination of the foregoing with many previous characteristics included is here illustrated by the Chapman bowl (No. 154) predominantly in yellow and puce, the loose bouquet with cotton stems, and the roses with wiped-out highlights and a border of tightly packed pink and yellow roses. This belongs to the same group as the WILLIAM TAYLOR mug, 1759 and the ROBERTS bowl, 1761. There is a painter at work on pieces in this group who frequently used striped yellow and pink tulips, sometimes closed and

looking like a striped damson (No. 156) or with one divergent petal (No. 155)
(6) a group which is heavily outlined and in a slightly less vivid palette than the
preceding, seen here in Nos. 166 and 167 showing close links with group 3
(7) The final group is perhaps derived from Worcester, with cramped bouquets
with messy, muddy-green foliage beneath iron-red loop and dot rims (Nos.
169–171).

Clearly the flower painting could be looked at in more detail but the groups
referred to above might be used as a framework on which to build a comparative
study.

There are a number of pieces made towards the end of the 1760s, many bearing
iron-red anchor and dagger marks, which are now generally considered to be
the work of an independent decorator outside the factory. Previously this group
has been associated with Giles and his atelier but in view of the variation in
treatment, and the lack of similarity in style to the Grubbe plates, it would seem
that more than one individual or atelier was responsible.

Although unmarked, the LIBERTY bowl (No. 172) is an especially important
link, first in its similarity to the well-documented HALLIFAX-LODGE bowl, but
also to an anchor and dagger marked blue-ground sauceboat in the Museum of
London with similar fruit painting. The oval basketwork dishes (No. 176) do,
however, show close links with factory flower painting, suggesting that a factory
painter should not be entirely ruled out. The exotic bird painting is
characteristic of this group at first quite simply drawn (No. 178) and then in a
fussier style and in combination with blue and blue-scale grounds (Nos. 173 and
174). As with the blue and white section, which must be considered to represent
a large part of the factory's production, it is difficult to attribute pieces in this
group to a date much later than 1770 though there could be a case for dating
these pieces later than generally accepted.

Another piece worthy of particular mention is the remarkable bottle (No. 163),
illustrated here in colour plate VI. It was first pointed out to me by Simon
Spero, whose astute observation I gratefully acknowledge, that this may
perhaps be by Fidelle Duvivier. There are certainly marked similarities between
this bottle and the Caughley tea-wares discussed by Geoffrey Godden
('Caughley Teawares Painted by Fidelle Duvivier; The Missing Link', *The
Antique Dealer and Collectors Guide*, August 1978). The treatment of the hair almost
as though the figures have mop wigs, the way in which the folds in the clothing
are denoted by shading, the treatment of the trees and the brown rocks with
scrubby foliage in the foreground and the sky with groups of birds in flight, all
point to a possible Duvivier attribution. Attribution on these grounds alone is of
course rather tenuous, but if this piece can be attributed on style alone, then it
implies Duvivier was probably working in London at an outside decorating
establishment or possibly at the Bow factory before his departure for Derby in
1769.

126 Fork-handle the porcelain *c.* 1753
of pistol shape, painted in black with figures
in a boat among river islands within
turquoise foliage and scroll cartouches
suspending swags of pink and red flowers
with yellow centres, fitted with a steel three-
pronged fork and silver ferrule.
3¾ in long

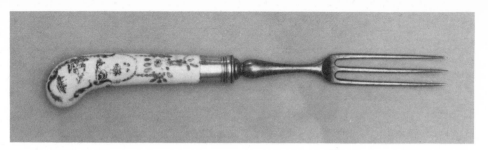

126

**127 Six crested knife-handles and six
fork-handles** the porcelain 1753–55
each of pistol form and moulded with shells,
C-scrolls and swags of foliage, the tops
painted with the crest of *an erased falcon's head,
langued gules*, the upper part moulded with
stiff leaves and edged in puce and gilding,
fitted with steel knives joined by silver
ferrules, the steel knives marked 'Wood
York'.
4 in long

Provenance:

Anon., sale Sotheby's, 31 May 1977, lot 130

The crest is perhaps that of Davidson of Balgay, Scotland

The firm of Joseph Wood commenced business at
Spurrigate, York in 1799. By 1843 they were listed as
cutlers, gunsmiths and surgical instrument makers under
the title of Joseph Wood & Sons. The firm's name
changing to Joseph Wood & Co. in 1871, under which
title they continued into the present century

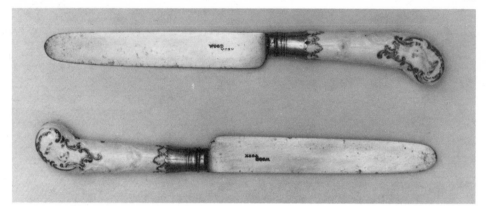

127

**128 Two crested knife-handles and two
fork-handles** *c.* 1755
painted in pale-puce, yellow, green and blue
with trailing flowers about gilt C-scrolls and
with the crest of *three ostrich feathers, erect
Argent, issuant from an Eastern Crown Or*, fitted
with steel three-pronged forks and curved
blades, joined by silver ferrules.
the knives 4¼ in and 3½ in long
the forks 4 in and 3½ in long

Provenance:

Anon., sale Sotheby's, 8 July 1980, lot 94,
from a complete set of twelve knives and
forks

The crest is perhaps that of Moses Mendes (who changed
his name to Head) grandson of Dr Fernando Mendes,
Physician to Charles II

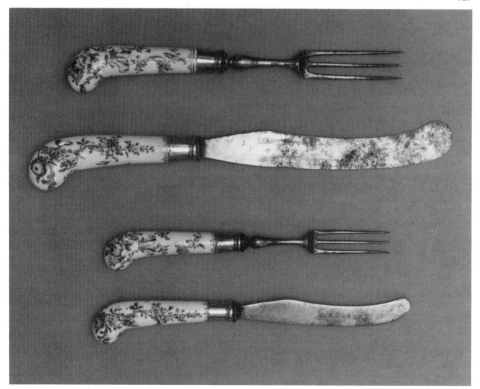

128

129 Scalloped botanical dish *c.* 1756
painted in a pale palette with a pink plant
with yellow-green leaves and puce stems and
with scattered flower-sprays and butterflies
within a chocolate line rim, the lower leaf
inscribed 'Bixa' in script.
8½ in diam.

Provenance:
Anon., sale Sotheby's, 20 December 1972, lot
105
Anon., sale Christie's, 21 March 1977, lot
129

Literature:
Adams (Elizabeth) and David Redstone: *Bow
Porcelain*, pl. 58

(where the authors have taken the inscription to read
Bisca.
This could well be the case as the plant seems nearer to
an Hibiscus than Bixa which is a plant indigenous to
tropical America)

129

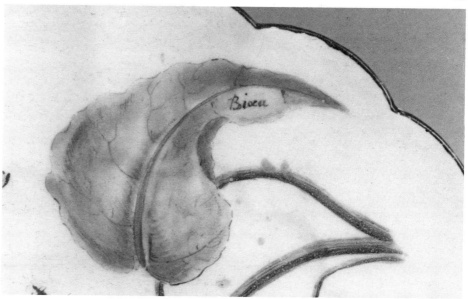

129 detail

130 A pair of octagonal botanical plates *c.* 1758
painted with a pink specimen flower with yellow-green leaves shaded in black, the rim with scattered butterflies and insects.
9 in diam.

Provenance:
The Countess of Lismore
Colonel Frank Falkenor

(then attributed to Chelsea, perhaps on the evidence of one of this series bearing a red anchor mark)

131 Rose-box and cover 1756–58
the pink-edged bloom applied with two insects, the cover with a pink bud and rose stock, the base with two buds.
3¼ in diam.

Provenance:
Anon., sale Christie's, 19 November 1979, lot 9, and there attributed to Derby

Cf. Savage (George): *18th Century English Porcelain,* pl. 5b for a Chelsea example

132 Campana vase with flowers *c.* 1758
painted with a pink, blue and iron-red
flower, scattered flower-sprays and insects
beneath a chocolate line and everted rim,
contemporaneously converted with pale Bow
flowers on *tôle-peinte* branches forming a pot
of flowers.
2 in high

Provenance:
Lord Suffield, Gunton Park, sale Irelands,
16 September 1980, part lot 721

Cf. No. 133

133 Small campana vase *c.* 1758
painted in puce, blue and yellow with
trailing flower-sprays beneath a chocolate
line rim, the everted rim with further flower-
sprays, on a circular spreading foot.
3 in high

Provenance:
Dr John Ainslie, sale Sotheby's, 7 March
1961, lot 132

132

133

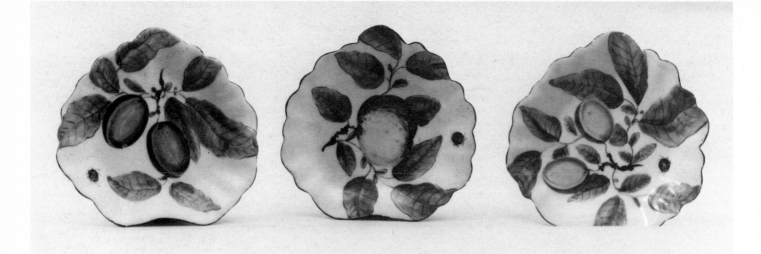

134

135

136

134 Three sweetmeat-dishes *c.* 1758
of lobed heart shape, each painted in the
botanical style with two plums, two damsons
and an apple, all with grey-green foliage and
a purple ladybird, within chocolate line rims.
4½ in wide

135 Circular pot and gadrooned cover
c. 1758
painted with pink and yellow roses and blue,
yellow and puce violets with grey-green
foliage, beneath chocolate rims, the cover
with a pink and blue bud finial.
3 in high

136 A pair of rococo candlesticks
1758–60
each of vase form, moulded with puce C-
scrolls and shells, painted with flower-sprays,
the nozzles with a band of applied coloured
flowers in puce, yellow and blue, the lobed
rims to the nozzles enriched in blue, on
circular spreading bases.
6¾ in high

Provenance:
Anon., sale Phillips, 7 February 1979, lot 126

No similar pair would appear to be recorded

137 Spherical bottle 1758–60
with narrow long neck painted in the
Meissen style in a pale palette of puce, blue
and yellow with a bouquet and scattered
flower-sprays, the top of the neck with puce
S-scrolls.
7½ in high

Cf. Nos. 144 and 149

137

138   139

138 Two-handled vase *c.* 1759

the tapering oviform body with green handles, flower terminals and pierced neck, painted with bouquets of flowers and flower-sprays in the Chelsea style within moulded C-scroll cartouches enriched in puce, blue and gilding, the lower part with trailing coloured flowers in relief surrounded by three putti scantily draped in turquoise, yellow and pink, two playing the pipes and one with a puppet, on a shaped scroll-moulded base enriched in puce, turquoise and gilding.
$7\frac{1}{2}$ in high

Provenance:

Anon., sale Sotheby's, 10 December 1973, lot 204

Similarly modelled to the Handel vase in the British Museum (1938, 3–14, 113) formerly in the Wallace Elliot Collection illustrated in the *Bow Porcelain Exhibition Catalogue, 1959*, fig. 36, no. 104
Cf. The Handel clock-case, No. 139

139 A Handel clock-case 1759

of shaped scroll-moulded outline edged with puce and turquoise foliage and shell-moulded scrolls, the front painted in puce with a score inscribed 'Minuetto' and with two coloured butterflies, the sides with scores inscribed 'A Cantata', 'Hay-makers', '. . . Handle' '. . . by Lorv' 'Sonata IV' 'A, Minuet' 'A Song' 'Fr Nov. 5. 1759' with bouquets above, surmounted by a figure of Time draped in puce and yellow, the sides with two putti, on a shaped rectangular base applied with a cockerel *impressed To mark*.
$12\frac{1}{4}$ in high

Provenance:

Mrs Donald J. Morrison, sale Sotheby's, 3 April 1973, lot 194

Exhibited:

E.C.C. Commemorative Exhibition 1977, no. 132

Cf. Tait (Hugh): 'Handel and Bow', *Apollo*, July 1962, pp. 384–90 *Bow Porcelain Exhibition Catalogue 1959*, fig. 36, no. 104
There is another example in the Cecil Higgins Museum, Bedford (c. 163)

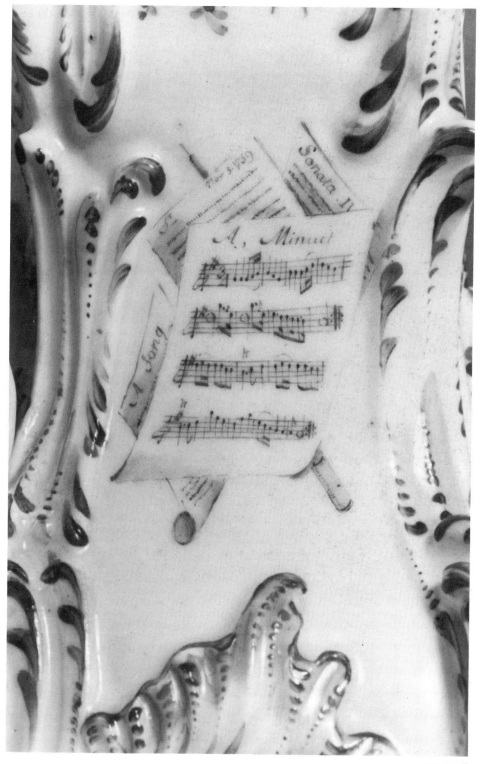

139 detail

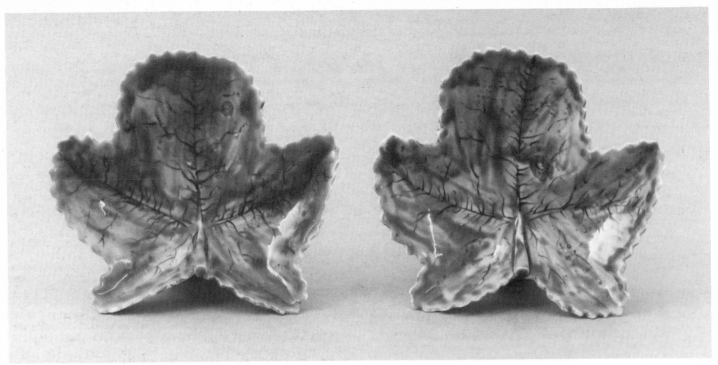

140

141

142

140 A pair of leaf-shaped pickle-dishes *c.* 1760
washed over in green enamel, the veins in a darker green within serrated rims, the underside with raised veins and one painted with four green leaves.
4¼ in wide

Provenance:
Lord Suffield, Gunton Park, sale Irelands, 16 September 1980, lot 792

141 Leaf-shaped pickle-dish *c.* 1760
en suite to the preceding (No. 140), but painted in a slightly greyer green enamel.
4¼ in wide

Provenance:
Lord Suffield, Gunton Park, sale Irelands, 16 September 1980, lot 793

142 Leaf-shaped pickle-dish *c.* 1760
painted in a pale grey-green with dark-brown veins within a serrated rim, the underside lightly modelled with veins.
4¾ in wide

143 A Blind Earl sweetmeat-dish *c.* 1760
the rose stock handle with pink bud terminals, moulded and coloured in tones of green with two branches, one of seven leaves, the other of six, with dark-brown veins, within a lobed black line rim.
5½ in diam.

This form is most usually found at Worcester, although there are Chelsea examples extant. It seems most probable that the present example was a special order, perhaps as a replacement, taken from a Meissen original

144 Sugar-bowl *c.* 1760
with slightly everted rim, painted with a bouquet of trailing garden flowers and three flower-sprays beneath a chocolate line rim.
4 in diam.

Cf. Nos. 137 and 149

143

144

145 Vine-leaf moulded sauceboat

c. 1760

the handle formed as a vinestock with grape and foliage terminal, the exterior modelled as overlapping leaves painted in tones of grey-green, green and yellow with puce veins, on an oval foot painted with puce C-scrolls, the interior with a spray of trailing vine, within a pink *feuille-de-choux* rim.

7 in wide

Cf. Watney (Bernard): *English Blue and White Porcelain of the 18th Century*, pl. 16A for a blue and white creamboat of similar form

145

146 Rococo scroll-moulded bowl *c.* 1760

of oval form the exterior enriched in puce with foliage and scroll moulding, the interior with a bouquet of garden flowers and scattered flower-sprays in tones of blue, yellow, iron-red and puce, on an oval scroll-moulded foot.

7 in wide

Exhibited:

E.C.C. Commemorative Exhibition 1977, no. 134

146

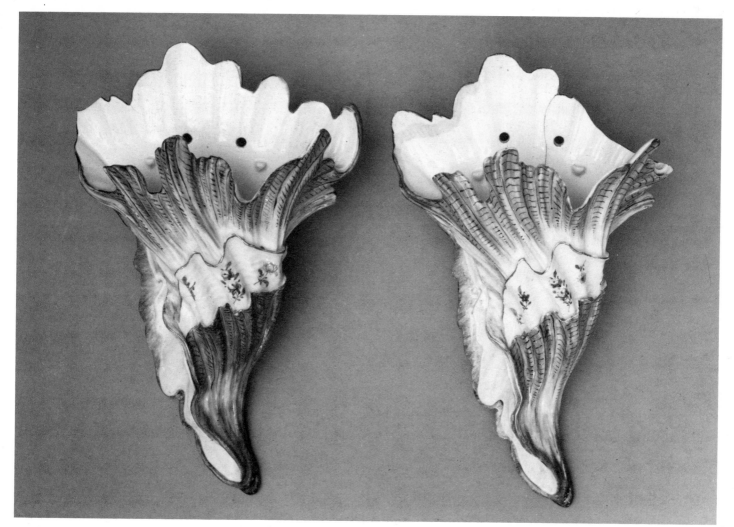

147 A pair of wall-pockets *c.* 1760
of rococo shell-moulded form, painted
predominantly in puce and enriched in pale-
blue and yellow, the central band left in the
white and painted with flower-sprays, lightly
edged in gilding.
11 in high

Provenance:
Anon., sale Sotheby's, 16 October 1962, lot
34
Anon., sale Phillips, 7 November 1979, lot
168

148

149

150, 151

148 Octagonal plate *c.* 1760
boldly painted with an Oriental seated
beneath a pine tree, wearing a black hat
and puce and blue robes beside a fence
and a yellow-topped, blue-edged table with
iron-red legs, a butterfly in flight above, the
border with grey-green grasses and trailing
foliage, within a chocolate line rim, the
reverse with a grey-green leaf to the rim.
8¾ in diam.

Provenance:
Anon., sale Sotheby's, 24 October 1978, lot
132

149 Octagonal plate *c.* 1760
painted in a blue, puce and yellow palette
with a central bouquet of flowers surrounded
by four flower-sprays within a chocolate rim.
8 in diam.

Cf. Nos. 137 and 144

150 A pair of flower-pots *c.* 1760
with cactus covers, the pots of bucket-form
painted with trailing garden flowers and
flower-sprays between two brown bands
moulded with yellow ring handles, the rims
with puce and yellow gadrooning, the covers
formed as open green-leaved cactus edged in
yellow, *the bases with incised nos. 26 and 28, the
covers with incised nos. 31 and 45.*
3½ in high

151 Flower-pot with cactus *c.* 1760
the bucket-shaped pot painted with flower-
sprays with two moulded brown bands
suspending four yellow ring handles, beneath
a puce and yellow gadrooned rim, the open
cactus with grey-green leaves.
4 in high

Provenance:
Lord Suffield, Gunton Park, sale Irelands,
16 September 1980, lot 721

**152 Pot-pourri bowl and pierced
cover** *c.* 1762
of faceted form, painted in a bold palette in
blue, puce and yellow with bouquets,
scattered flower-sprays and a tulip, with
moulded scroll handles and a chocolate line
rim, *painter's numeral 5.*
8 in diam.

Provenance:
Anon, sale Christie's, 21 April 1980, lot 112

Cf. Nos. 154 and 156

152

153

154 interior

153 Plate *c.* 1762
the centre painted in a pale palette with
puce, blue and yellow bouquets and scattered
flower-sprays within a shaped chocolate rim.
8½ in diam.

154 underside

154 Inscribed and dated bowl 1762
the exterior painted in a predominantly pale-
puce and yellow palette with tulips and
bouquets of garden flowers and scattered
flower-sprays with pale-green foliage, the
interior with a branch of two peaches, a
butterfly, two insects and a ladybird within a
border of tight garden flowers, the base
inscribed in puce 'MR. JOHN CHAPMAN,
1762', *painter's numeral 5.*
7 in diam.

Cf. Nos. 152 and 156
There are marked similarities between this bowl and the
JOHN AND ELIZABETH ROBERTS bowl dated 1761 in the Judge
Irwin Untermyer Collection and also the WILLIAM TAYLOR
mug dated 1759 in the Victoria & Albert Museum, both
illustrated in the *Bow Porcelain Exhibition Catalogue 1959*, figs
41, 42, 34 and 35

155 Kidney-shaped dish 1762–65
painted in the Meissen style with bouquets
and scattered garden flowers predominantly
in blue, puce, yellow, iron-red and with
foliage in tones of green, within a chocolate
line rim.
10½ in wide

This form is more usually associated with the Worcester
factory and it seems probable that this is a replacement for
a Worcester service, the painting, however, is typical of
Bow

156 Peach-shaped dish *c.* 1762
with pale-green stalk handle, boldly painted
in yellow, puce and blue with a flower-spray
including a closed tulip and scattered flowers
within a chocolate line rim.
10 in long

Provenance:
Anon., sale Christie's, 21 March 1977, lot
131

Cf. Nos. 152 and 154

155

156

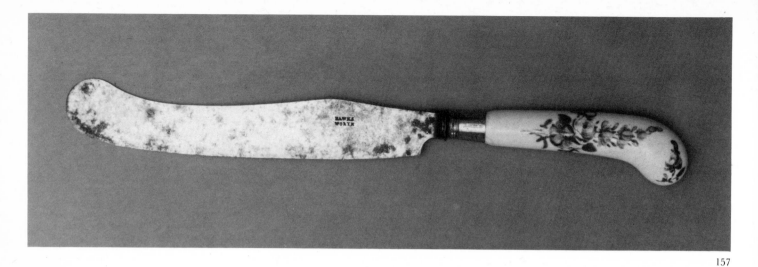

157 Knife-handle *c.* 1762
painted in a dry palette with blue, puce, yellow and red bouquets of flowers and two flower-sprays, fitted with a curved steel blade marked 'Hawks Worth'.
4 in long

Cf. The John Bowcock Memorandum Book 'July 24, 1756 ... The knife-handles: how many sold of Dresden flowers? and to have a double dozn, mounted'

158 Plate *c.* 1765
painted with a bunch of white grapes with leaves in tones of green and yellow edged in puce and with puce veins with a scattered ladybird and two insects, within a shaped chocolate rim.
8¾ in diam.

159 Pierced concave stand *c.* 1762
the sides painted with flower-sprays divided by three trellis-pattern panels with blue and yellow flowerheads, the rim with a puce line, with three feet moulded and coloured with puce and turquoise scrolls.
2¼ in high

160 A pair of vases of flowers *c.* 1765
the bucket-shaped vases painted with butterflies and insects in tones of puce, blue and yellow moulded with two bands, filled with flowers predominantly carnations and orange-blossom in similar tones with yellow-green foliage.
7 in high

Cf. Savage (George) & Harold Newman: *An Illustrated Dictionary of Ceramics*, p. 124 for a similar example in the Smithsonian Institute, Washington DC
Also another pair in the Museum of London (A7985)

159

160

161

161 Oval pierced two-handled basket and cover *c.* 1765
with green rope-twist handles, the interior painted with two pears on a branch, the exterior applied with blue flowerheads with yellow centres on an elaborate scroll-moulded base enriched in green and puce, applied with coloured flowers with green foliage and black veins, the cover modelled as a dome of garden flowers enriched in natural pale colours.
7 in high

Cf. Rackham (Bernard): *Schreiber Collection Catalogue*, pl. 13, no. 51, for another example but lacking the cover

162 A pair of frill-vases and covers
c. 1765
with female-mask and foliage handles, painted with scattered insects and applied with brightly coloured garden flowers in yellow, puce and blue, a band of corn enriched in puce connecting the handles, the lower part with a band of coloured petals, the pierced necks with yellow-centred blue flowerheads, the covers with bird finials.
11 in high

Cf. a similar pair in the Museum of London (A9700)

162

163 Pear-shaped bottle *c.* 1765
painted in the manner of *Fidelle Duvivier* in a
pale-pink, blue and yellow palette with four
boys, two with a bird in a birdcage and the
others reading by a river, in wooded glades,
surrounded by applied garden flowers
enriched in pale colours, painted with
scattered insects, the bulbous neck and foot
with yellow-centred blue flowers.
10 in high

Provenance:
Anon., sale Christie's, 16 June 1975, lot 94

Cf. Watney (Bernard): *English Blue and White Porcelain of
the 18th Century*, pl. 17A for blue and white examples of this
type
See Introductory Text p. 87 for a short discussion
concerning the tentative attribution to Duvivier

163

163 detail or reverse

164

165

164 Leaf-dish *c.* 1765
with green stalk handle moulded and
coloured with two sprays of gooseberries
resting on three grey-green leaves, the main
leaf with incised veins enriched in puce
within a serrated yellow-green rim.
6½ in wide

The form is known in both saltglaze and Lowestoft
although not previously recorded at Bow

165 Baluster mug *c.* 1765
the grooved loop handle with heart-shaped
terminal painted in a pale famille rose palette
with two Orientals in pale-pink, blue and
yellow clothes, one with a branch, the other
carrying a vase, standing beside a scale-
pattern table and flanked by trees and
flowering shrubs issuing from pierced pale-
yellow and blue rockwork beneath a
chocolate line rim.
5½ in high

Provenance:
Anon., sale Christie's, 9 February 1981, lot
158

**166 Miniature part tea- and coffee-
service** *c.* 1765
painted with bouquets and scattered flowers
in puce, yellow, blue and tones of green,
comprising:
A globular teapot and cover, 5 in wide
A sugar-bowl and cover 2½ in diam.
A pear-shaped cream-jug 2½ in high
Two coffee-cups and saucers

Provenance:
J. Warrell, sale Sotheby's, 13 February 1979,
lot 99

167 Globular teapot and cover *c.* 1765
painted in a yellow, puce and blue palette
with a bouquet and scattered flower-sprays,
the cover with a chocolate line rim.
5 in high

Provenance:
Anon., sale Phillips, 7 November 1979,
lot 167

166

167

168

170, 169

171

168 Leaf-dish 1765–70
painted in a dry palette in pale-yellow, blue, puce and green with a bouquet and scattered flowers, resting on a green-edged leaf with puce veins.
9 in long

169 Baluster cream-jug 1765–68
with small grooved loop handle, painted in a pale palette of yellow, pink, iron-red and green with flower-sprays and scattered flowers beneath an iron-red loop, line and dot-pattern rim.
3 in high

170 Bowl 1765–68
en suite to the preceding (No. 169).
5 in diam.

171 A pair of small mugs 1765–68
with grooved loop handles, painted with a bouquet and scattered garden flowers, in blue, puce, yellow and iron-red beneath an iron-red loop, line and dot-pattern border.
About 2½ in high
Cf. Nos. 169 and 170

172 Inscribed green-ground bowl
1767–68
the exterior boldly painted with grapes, peaches, apples, strawberries and other fruit with green foliage, within gilt C-scroll cartouches, reserved on an uneven sea-green ground, the interior inscribed 'LIBERTY' in underglaze-blue with a flowerhead and flourish to the left, between two iron-red carp, the rim richly gilt with C-scrolls and foliage.
10 in diam.

Literature:
Freeman (G. A. L.): 'Bow Liberty Bowl', *Antique Collecting*, September 1981
Ainslie (John A.): 'Inscribed and dated Bow', *Apollo*, January 1955

Cf. Adams (Elizabeth) and David Redstone: *Bow Porcelain*, pp. 75 and 187, pls. 12A and B, where a bowl with a similar painting inscribed HALLIFAX-LODGE NORTH-CAROLINA is described and illustrated. Also *op. cit.* pl. 114 for a sauceboat with similar painting with an anchor and dagger mark

172

172 interior

173

174

175

173 A pair of blue-ground plates *c.* 1770
the centres painted with exotic birds strutting
and perched among shrubs in tones of blue,
pink and yellow, the washed underglaze-blue
borders enriched with gilt flower-sprays
within shaped gilt line rims, the undersides
with gilt foliage covering imperfections in the
body, *iron-red anchor and dagger marks.*
8 in diam.

Provenance:
Wallace Elliott
Frances L. Dickson

174 Blue-scale plate *c.* 1770
painted with exotic birds, berried foliage and
insects within gilt vase and mirror-shaped
cartouches on a blue-scale ground within a
shaped gilt line rim, *blue square seal mark and
anchor and dagger mark in gold.*
8 in diam.

Provenance:
Robert Drane
Herbert Eccles
Wallace Elliot, sale Sotheby's, 25 May 1938,
lot 230

Cf. the blue-scale teapot and cover dated 1761, though
possibly of later date, in the Glynn Vivian Art Gallery,
Swansea and illustrated in *The Bow Exhibition Catalogue,
1959,* fig. 38, no. 106
This type of decoration is more normally associated with
the Worcester factory, the presence of a square seal mark
suggests that it may have been made as a replacement for
a Worcester service

175 Plate *c.* 1770
the centre with an underglaze-blue eight-
pointed star enriched in gilding surrounded
by two branches in different tones of green,
on which perch two birds with
predominantly yellow, orange and pink
plumage and with scattered butterflies and a
yellow insect, within a flattened lobed rim,
anchor and dagger mark in iron-red.
7¾ in diam.

Cf. *Untermyer Collection Catalogue,* pl. 88, no. 268, for an
écuelle and stand similarly painted

176 A pair of lobed oval dishes 1765–70
the centres painted in puce, yellow, iron-red
and blue with a bouquet of flowers within a
moulded gilt oval cartouche surrounded by
moulded triangular panels within a deeply
moulded trellis-pattern border reserved with
panels of flower-sprays, *iron-red anchor and
dagger marks.*
7 in wide

176

177 Flared and fluted pierced vase

c. 1770

painted with a girl with a birdcage walking among shrubs and foliage, the reverse with a bird strutting among shrubs, within gilt ogival cartouches, with two cartouches of flowers above and two below with two gilt insects between, gilt line rims.

6¾ in high

Cf. No. 179

Rackham (Bernard): *The Herbert Allen Collection,* pl. 5, no. 11

178 Oval two-handled basket c. 1768

the centre painted with an exotic bird in blue, yellow, puce and iron-red perched on a berried flowering branch within a border of scattered flower-sprays, the green double rope-twist handles with flower terminals, the exterior with moulded basket weave, *iron-red anchor and dagger mark.*

6¾ in long

179 Four-footed scroll-moulded stand

c. 1770

the sides painted with four panels of exotic birds in predominantly blue, puce, iron-red and yellow strutting among grey-green foliage divided by four scroll feet enriched in turquoise and gilding, beneath a scroll-moulded border enriched in gilding, *iron-red anchor and dagger mark.*

6¼ in wide

Cf. Stoner (Frank): *Chelsea, Bow and Derby Porcelain Figures,* pl. 102

180 Cylindrical mug c. 1770

the grooved loop handle with heart-shaped terminal, painted with exotic birds perched and strutting among berried foliage beneath an elaborate iron-red scroll and loop-pattern border and line rim.

4½ in high

Cf. Rackham (Bernard): *Schreiber Collection Catalogue,* pl. 13, no. 107

177

178

179

180

181 Shallow teacup and saucer *c.* 1770
the body with pinecone moulding between
sea-green borders, the centre of the cup and
saucer with a flower-spray with gilt foliage
within a gilt line rim, *the teacup with iron-red
anchor and dagger mark.*

A similar coffee-cup and saucer was formerly in Dr John
Ainslie's collection, sale Sotheby's, 7 March 1961, lot 41
Cf. No. 182

181

182 Oviform teacaddy *c.* 1770
the body with pinecone moulding between
sea-green borders, the top rim enriched in
gilding, *iron-red anchor and dagger mark.*
4 in high

182

Figures

The production of figures is the main area where Bow may be considered consistently successful.

As previously seen when considering the wares, many of the earliest pieces were left in the white, the sculptural quality of the material being shown to best advantage. The earliest documentary figures are the Henry Woodward and Kitty Clive in the Untermyer and Fitzwilliam Collections, dated 1750 and also the Negress with a basket in the Katz Collection. These are represented here and illustrate how the paste can vary from a rich cream to a grey-white at this early date and how the colour of paste or glaze should not therefore be used as a sole criterion for dating. There are marked similarities in modelling (see particularly Nos. 183 and 184) which, apart from the basketwork bowls, have applied flowering branches and flowers with the same raised beaded centres. The group of two boys playing with a dolphin (No. 185) is from a Meissen or Vincennes original, yet based on a bronze; these chubby-cheeked putti with their thick sausage-like limbs appear again with the bowl and cover (No. 183). These early figures do not form a distinct and conglomerate group being derived from engravings (Kitty Clive and Henry Woodward), sculpture in bronze or terracotta (the dolphin group already mentioned and the sphinxes, No. 189) and sometimes from Meissen originals taken in their turn from engravings, for example No. 191.

The source for the so-called Mongolians is unknown, although Dr Bellamy Gardner in a paper to the E.C.C. (see footnote to No. 188) discussed a possible source in a pair of rococo wall-brackets. These must surely be considered as the faotory's greatest *tour de force* using the material with enormous sculptural success.

Another group in a rather different vein are the figures associated with the Muses. This modeller remains unidentified. His work has certain well-documented characteristics, here illustrated by three Muses (Nos. 197, 198 and 200), Juno and Jupiter (No. 199), the group of Ki Mao Sao (No. 195), the Fortune Teller (No. 196) and Matrimony (No. 201). The Muses are characterised by neatly dressed hair, usually clearly shaded and sometimes drawn back in a bun or hanging in plaits. They are not paragons of beauty, having aquiline noses and no chins, yet the drapery is used to good effect, hanging naturally in folds suggesting the form beneath. When coloured, they have long brown eyebrows, their nostrils appear as two darkened commas and they have parted red lips. The palette is soft and laid on in broad streaky washes in pale-brown, puce and a distinctive pale lemon-yellow – this last colour is particularly clear in Urania (No. 200 and colour plate VIII). Euterpe and

Matrimony both have small enamelled flower-sprays. The source for the Muses are perhaps French engravings, many figures being incised in a corrupted French with the Muses' name.

The mainstream of figure production chiefly comprises sets of Seasons, Continents, Elements, Senses, Sporters, Cooks, Musicians, Monks and Nuns, many inspired by Meissen originals. The bases began by being of simple pad or mound form, giving way to bases with simple scroll painting or moulding, the palette, in line with the wares, similarly changes to a vivid, brighter style including the puce, yellow and turquoise previously referred to under the section dealing with European decoration. The musician (No. 221) is especially interesting, showing the Chelsea style of flower painting in combination with an opaque turquoise bodice and a slightly more elaborate scroll-moulded base associated with the late 1750s that gives way to the four-footed scroll bases of the 1760s, many with flowering trees and frequently with underglaze-blue and gilding and bearing anchor and dagger marks. These anchor and dagger marked figures sometimes occur with an underglaze-blue A mark. The candlestick-figures (No. 241) are noteable, as apart from the underglaze-blue painting, they were most probably mounted and decorated elsewhere. Many Bow figures have a square hole at the back, deliberately made to take a *tôle-peinte* branch mounted with flowers or to hold a candle-nozzle. Some pieces bear an impressed T or To mark which has traditionally been attributed to Mr Tebo, a repairer, who was referred to in unglowing terms by Josiah Wedgwood in correspondence with his partner Thomas Bentley (letter of 3 July 1775). This mark which not only appears on Bow (up to about 1765) but also on Worcester, and Champion's Bristol porcelain, and perhaps on Caughley, has recently been connected with the Toulouse family of modellers from France (see Geoffrey Godden: *Caughley and Worcester Porcelains, 1775–1800*, pl. 10, and Henry Sandon: *Flight and Barr Worcester Porcelains 1783–1840*, p. 208). Knowledge of this family and their connection with the use of these impressed marks is still inconclusive; however, Elizabeth Adams and David Redstone have placed their evidence and their conclusions on record (*Bow Porcelain*, pp. 140 and 141).

The late figures are frequently adaptations of earlier models mounted on pierced scroll bases (Nos. 228 and 229 with the set No. 245). The modelling becomes progressively lumpier and the limbs wooden in appearance, the heads sometimes absurdly small in relation to the rest of the body, the blown cheeks are sometimes highlighted in an iron-red, the clothing is no longer made to fit the body so that it reveals little of the form beneath. These figures and groups are contemporary with the Chelsea figures of the gold anchor period and made to appeal to the same market, which had almost disappeared by the late 1760s with the closure of the Chelsea factory.

183 A white group of two putti with a bowl and cover *c.* 1750
seated on a shaped rockwork base supporting the basketwork bowl and cover, the cover and base applied with flowering branches beneath a creamy glaze.
10 in wide

Provenance:
Aubrey Toppin, sale Sotheby's, 19 May 1970, lot 11

Cf. *Bow Porcelain Exhibition Catalogue, 1959*, no. 45 for a similar example from the D. A. MacAlister Collection
Also No. 184

184 Negress with a basket and cover
c. 1750
modelled as a naked girl, her lower part covered by a cloth, her arms open towards an oval basketwork bowl and cover, with flower-branch finial, on an oval rockwork base applied with trailing foliage and flowerheads.
8¾ in high

Cf. *Bow Porcelain Exhibition Catalogue, 1959*, fig. 6, no. 44 for the example from the Katz Collection, incised with the date 1750
Toppin (Aubrey): 'Bow Porcelain, Some Recent Excavations on the Site of the Factory', *Burlington Magazine*, May 1922, figs. G & H
Aubrey Toppin, sale Sotheby's, 19 May 1970, lot 12
Adams (Elizabeth) and David Redstone: *Bow Porcelain*, pl. 61 for the example in the Museum of London
After a Meissen model first conceived by Eberlein in 1741

185 A white group of two scantily draped boys playing with a dolphin
c. 1750
with lightly incised hair, the dolphin with incised scales, on an oval rockwork base applied with flowers and foliage.
7 in high

Taken from a Meissen or Vincennes original and copied at the English factories of Chelsea, Bow and Longton Hall. For a Longton Hall example cf. Tilley (Frank): *Teapots and Tea*, pl. LXIII, no. 187
Another Bow example is in the Glaisher Collection (no. 3028) in the Fitzwilliam Museum, Cambridge and a coloured version at the Passmore Edwards Museum, East London

183

184

185

186 187

186 White figure of Kitty Clive *c.* 1750
in the rôle of 'The Fine Lady' from Garrick's
farce 'Lethe' in lace cap, lace-edged jacket
and wide crinoline, holding a spaniel beneath
her right arm, on a square base.
10½ in high

For the companion figure see No. 187
Cf. *Untermyer Collection Catalogue*, pl. 76, fig. 241
Bow Porcelain Exhibition Catalogue, 1959, figs. 18 & 19, no.
40 for the example in the Fitzwilliam Museum,
Cambridge dated 1750
The model is taken from an engraving by Charles Mosley
published in 1750, based on an earlier drawing by
Worlidge

187 White figure of Henry Woodward
c. 1750
in the rôle of 'The Fine Gentleman' from
Garrick's farce 'Lethe' wearing a tricorn hat,
a jacket and waistcoat, with traces of cold-
fired gilding, and tight breeches, his sword
behind his leg, standing before a ruined pillar
on a square base incised with diamond-
pattern, *incised star mark beneath the base.*
10½ in high

For the companion figure see No. 186
Cf. *Untermyer Collection Catalogue*, pl. 77, fig. 241, for the
example dated 1750, and pp. 168 & 169 for an extensive
list of similar examples
The model is taken from an undated mezzotint by James
McArdell from a painting by Francis Hayman

**188 A pair of white busts of
Mongolians** *c.* 1750
with Oriental features, wearing plumed and
jewelled foliage headwear and lace and
feather collars, their bodices elaborately
moulded with frogging in the form of
strapwork, on circular spreading socles with
concave bases.
he 10¾ in high
she 10½ in high

Provenance:
Lord Suffield, Gunton Park, sale Irelands,
16 September 1980, lot 774

Cf. Adams (Elizabeth) and David Redstone: *Bow Porcelain*,
pl. 69, where slightly different models are illustrated, he
with a drooping moustache and his companion with two
rows of beads to her necklace
Untermyer Collection Catalogue, pl. 79, fig. 242 for a coloured
pair
Savage (George): *18th Century English Porcelain*, pl. 42
Bellamy Gardner (Dr H): '18th Century Porcelain and
the Allied Arts', *E.P.C. Transactions*, vol. II, p. 20 where he
indicates a connection between these busts and a pair of
contemporary wall-brackets
There is a cryptic reference in the John Bowcock
Memorandum Book 'April 28, 1756, Think of the Chinese
head for Mr. Weatherby' which could perhaps relate to
these

189

189 A pair of white sphinxes *c.* 1750
to left and right, each with a lady's head
wearing a lace cap, ear rings and a necklace,
exposing her bare breast, with lion-shaped
paws appearing from lace-work cuffs, with
elaborate saddles on their backs, their tails
beneath their hind quarters and arched over
their backs, on shaped rococo scroll-work
bases.
$5\frac{1}{2}$ in long

Cf. Savage (George): *18th Century English Porcelain*, pl. 39
for a coloured pair, now in the Museum of Fine Arts,
Boston (445.1973a–b)
Rackham (Bernard): *Schreiber Collection Catalogue*, pl. 9, no.
143
Hobson (R. L.): *British Museum Collection Catalogue*, p. 8,
fig. 2
For a detailed dissertation concerning the Bow sphinxes,
cf. Tait (Hugh): 'Some Consequences of the Bow Special
Exhibition Part III – The Alderman Arnold and Thomas
Frye Periods (1748–1759)', *Apollo*, June 1960, where he
suggests they are probably derived from a French print or
engraving and discusses the distinguishing characteristics
between the earlier (as above) and later versions

190 White figure of a huntsman toper
1750–52
in wide-brimmed hat, his jacket and
waistcoat undone holding a flask and a glass,
spread on a mound base applied with dead
game, foliage and rustic implements, the
lower part applied with trailing foliage and
flowerheads with four radiating leaves.
$4\frac{3}{4}$ in high

There is another example of this figure in the collection of
Earl Spencer at Althorp, Northamptonshire which, unlike
the present example, is of a rich creamy colour

190

191 White figure of a bagpiper 1750–52
in wide-brimmed hat, billowing cloak,
unbuttoned waistcoat revealing his shirt and
breeches, playing his two-piped instrument
on an oval base applied with trailing flowers
and foliage.
9 in high

Cf. Savage (George): *18th Century English Porcelain*, pl. 57
for the example in the Museum of Fine Arts, Boston
(1959–1081)
After the Meissen model first conceived by J. J. Kaendler
in 1741, taken from a print engraved by Daullé after J.
Dumont le Romain

**192 White figure of a girl with a
cradle** 1750–52
in tight-fitting cap, bodice and apron,
holding a baby in a cradle, the arch incised
with a trailing flower, standing before a short
tree-stump on a rectangular base with canted
corners, *the base with incised arrow and annulet
mark.*
6 in high

Provenance:
Miss Beryl Statham, sale Sotheby's, 27 April
1976, lot 68

Cf. Adams (Elizabeth) and David Redstone: *Bow Porcelain*,
pl. 126 where a similar figure appears with a companion
playing the hurdy-gurdy

191

192

193 A pair of white figures of a sportsman and companion *c.* 1752
seated to left and right leaning on tree-stumps and holding guns, with dogs at their feet, on square rockwork bases.
5¾ in high

Provenance:
Anon., sale Phillips, 7 November 1979, lot 172

Cf. Similar examples from the Wallace Elliot Collection, sale Sotheby's, 25 May 1938, lot 208
Also *E.C.C. Transactions*, vol. 7, pt. 2, pls. 129B & C for a pair in white biscuit. Although biscuit figures and wares do not seem to have been a standard part of the Bow output, there is a contemporary reference in the John Bowcock Memorandum Book 'Mrs Whitfield to have one pr. white biscuit candlesticks May 15, 1756'

194 A white group of a lover and companion 1750–52
she playing the hurdy-gurdy and wearing a flowing dress, he to her right serenading his companion, in frilled hat and flowing jacket, on a shaped oval rockwork base applied with two flowers with three leaves.
4½ in high

Cf. *Untermyer Collection Catalogue* pls. 90 & 91, fig. 240 for two views of a coloured example of the more frequently found model, of which the present example has some similar features; also see *Bow Exhibition Catalogue 1959*, fig. 15, no. 48A, for the hand of the same modeller
Toppin (Aubrey): 'The Origin of Some Ceramic Designs', *E.C.C. Transactions*, vol. 2, no. 10 1948, pl. 103
Inspired by a Meissen original from an engraving by C. N. Cochin after the painting '*Belles, N'ecoutez Rien ou Arlequin Amoureux*' by Watteau

193

194

195 A group of the Goddess Ki Mao Sao 1750-52

with two attendants, she with her hair elaborately dressed and wearing a pale-yellow jacket and pale-pink dress edged in gilding, the two kneeling attendants with white robes enriched with pale-red flowerheads and green foliage, on a scroll-moulded base applied with blue flowers and green foliage, the moulding enriched in brown and gilding, about a central oval cartouche with puce mock Oriental characters, the reverse lightly enriched with green moss, *the base with E mark in red.*
10¾ in long

Provenance:
Anon., sale Sotheby's, 26 November 1974, lot 132

Exhibited:
E.C.C. Commemorative Exhibition, 1977, no. 136

Cf. Savage (George): *18th Century English Porcelain*, pl. 45A
Untermyer Collection Catalogue, pl. 80, fig. 243
Adams (Elizabeth) and David Redstone: *Bow Porcelain*, pl. 71
Taken from a design by Watteau engraved by M. Aubert, *c.* 1731, cf. E. Dacier and A. Vuaflart: *Jean de Jullienne et les Graveurs de Watteau au XVIIIe Siècle*, vol. IV, pl. 260

195

196 A group of the Fortune Teller *c.* 1752

modelled as a bearded gallant, a berried wreath in his hair in a pink and iron-red lined yellow coat, pale-turquoise breeches and black boots, his companion with dressed brown hair, a dark-green bodice with an applied wreath of flowers and a pale-pink dress, standing on a rectangular rockwork base applied with a blue flower with green leaves. [The painting perhaps of later date]
9½ in high

Provenance:
Aubrey Toppin, sale Sotheby's, 19 May 1970, lot 1
Anon., sale Bonham's, 25 March 1977, lot 73

Exhibited:
E.C.C. Exhibition, 1948, pl. 36, no. 163

Taken from an engraving by P. Aveline called 'La Bonne Aventure' after a painting by Boucher
Cf. Stoner (Frank): *Chelsea, Bow and Derby Porcelain Figures*, pl. 67
Savage (George): *18th Century English Porcelain*, pl. 44, for the example in the Museum of Fine Arts, Boston (61-1282)
Adams (Elizabeth) and David Redstone: *Bow Porcelain*, pl. 70 for a white example

196

197 White figure of Polyhymnia

1750–52

the draped and winged Muse pointing with her left hand to an inscribed obelisk, a shaped shield incised with scale-pattern, a sword and a plumed helmet at her feet, on a rockwork base, the reverse inscribed 'Ploimnie'.

7 in high

Cf. *E.C.C. Exhibition Catalogue, 1948*, pl. 36, no. 162
Adams (Elizabeth) and David Redstone: *Bow Porcelain*, pl. 64
Toppin (A. J.): 'Early Bow Muses', *Burlington Magazine*, April 1929 where he suggests this is not a figure of Polyhymnia but 'Winged Victory'
There is a coloured version in the Museum of Fine Arts, Boston (468–1973)

198 Figure of Euterpe 1750–52

the seated Muse with her hair tied in two plaits, wearing a puce and yellow-lined dress painted with pink and yellow flowers, holding a cornet, with other musical instruments at her side, on a shaped rockwork base.

6 in high

Provenance:
James McG. Stewart, sale Sotheby's, 13 November 1973, lot 47

Cf. *E.C.C. Exhibition Catalogue, 1948*, pl. 36, no 161
Lane (Arthur): *English Porcelain Figures of the 18th Century*, pl. 39
Adams (Elizabeth) and David Redstone: *Bow Porcelain*, pl. 66 for a white example
There is another coloured example in the Museum of Fine Arts, Boston (466–1973)

199 A pair of figures of Juno and Jupiter 1750–52

characteristically painted in washed enamels, Jupiter with streaked grey hair and puce cloak, holding a gilt sceptre with a massive brown eagle at his side, Juno in a puce-washed lemon-yellow and white dress, a peacock at her side, both on shaped rockwork bases.

Jupiter 6 in high
Juno 5½ in high

Provenance:
James McG. Stewart, sale Sotheby's, 13 November 1973, lot 49

Cf. Stoner (Frank): *Chelsea, Bow and Derby Porcelain Figures*, pl. 65 and Savage (George): *18th Century English Porcelain*, pl. 46A for a single figure of Juno

197

198

199

200 Figure of Urania 1750–52
standing in a lemon-yellow veil and puce-
washed lemon-yellow and white dress
marking out a globe with a pair of dividers,
resting on rockwork, on a square base.
6 in high

Provenance:
James McG. Stewart, sale Sotheby's,
13 November 1973, lot 50

Cf. Savage (George): *18th Century English Porcelain*, pl. 55C
E.C.C. Exhibition Catalogue, 1948, pl. 36, no. 160
Adams (Elizabeth) and David Redstone: *Bow Porcelain*,
pl. 62 for the Castle Howard example

201 Figure of Matrimony 1752–54
in pink-lined yellow hat, yellow jacket, black
bodice, pink sash, and a plain dress applied
with flower-sprays with gilt centres and
edged in gold, holding a gilt and brown
birdcage, standing beside a green rockwork
fountain with blue water, with a sheep
recumbent at her side, on a scroll-moulded
base enriched in green.
9½ in high

Provenance:
Anon., sale Sotheby's, 26 November 1974, lot
135

Cf. Stoner (Frank): *Chelsea, Bow and Derby Porcelain Figures*,
pl. 70
Savage (George): *18th Century English Porcelain*, pl. 60A, for
the example in the Museum of Fine Arts, Boston (65–1782)
Lane (Arthur): *English Porcelain Figures of the 18th Century*,
pl. 44
Hurlbutt (Frank): *Bow Porcelain*, pl. 39
Loosely based on a contemporary Meissen model by J. J.
Kaendler

202 Two figures of The Continents
c. 1755
America modelled as a negress in feathered
headdress and chiton and scantily draped in
pale-yellow and pink with a quiver of arrows
at her shoulder, standing before a crocodile,
Africa in elephant headdress and yellow-
edged white cloak standing before a
recumbent lion, both on shaped bases.
4 in high

200

201

202

203

204

203 White figure of a toper 1753–55
in conical hat, buttoned jacket and breeches,
standing with his right hand raised, his left
with a jug, seated on a tree-stump on a
circular pad base.
4½ in high

For a similar example cf. Aubrey Toppin, sale Sotheby's,
19 May 1970, lot 10 and a coloured example Bradshaw
(Peter): *18th Century English Porcelain Figures*, pl. 65

204 White figure of Winter *c.* 1755
modelled as an old man in a hooded coat
leaning on a stick warming his hands over a
brazier, seated on logs on a shaped mound
base with traces of cold-fired enamelling.
4¾ in high

205 Figure of Spring *c.* 1755
modelled as a girl in wide-brimmed black
hat, blue-cuffed puce bodice, flowered apron
and skirt with two pale-yellow baskets of
coloured flowers on a rockwork-pad base
painted with flowers, *iron-red E mark*.
5 in high

Cf. Savage (George): *18th Century English Porcelain*, pl. 64
Rackham (Bernard): *Herbert Allen Collection Catalogue*, pl. 2,
fig. 4

205, 206, 207

208

206 Figure of Autumn *c.* 1755
modelled as a youth in black hat, pink jacket, white shirt and flowered breeches, squeezing grapes into a skillet, seated on a lemon-yellow basket of grapes with a flask between his feet, on a pad base painted with foliage.
5¾ in high

Cf. Savage (George): *18th Century English Porcelain*, pl. 64
Lane (Arthur): *English Porcelain Figures of the 18th Century*, pl. 49

207 Figure of Winter *c.* 1755
modelled as a bearded old man in blue-cuffed pale-pink coat and flowered pale-yellow breeches warming his hands over a brazier on a circular pad base painted with a puce rose.
5 in high

Cf. Hurlbutt (Frank): *Bow Porcelain*, pl. 52, for a later example on a scroll base
Lane (Arthur): *English Porcelain Figures of the 18th Century*, pl. 50b
Savage (George): *18th Century English Porcelain*, pl. 64
Also No. 204 for a white example and Nos. 205 and 206 for examples of Spring and Autumn

209

208 A set of four busts of The Seasons *c.* 1755
modelled as the head and shoulders of Gods and Goddesses, Spring and Summer draped in puce with flowers and corn in their hair, Autumn as a bearded God with a garland of grapes in his hair and draped in bright blue and yellow, Winter as a bearded old man in an ermine-lined puce drape, on pale yellow and puce marbled pedestals, terminating on square bases.
5½ in high

Cf. Hurlbutt (Frank): *Bow Porcelain*, pl. 47A
Adams (Elizabeth) and David Redstone: *Bow Porcelain*, pl. 125

209 Figure of a girl *c.* 1756
emblematic of Autumn, in pink-lined yellow hat, green bodice, pale-pink apron and pale-yellow dress, seated holding a basket of grapes on her left knee on an oval scroll-moulded base enriched in puce.
5 in high

Cf. *E.C.C. Exhibition Catalogue, 1948*, pl. 38, no. 173

210

212

211

213

210 White figure of a seated nun *c.* 1755
in flowing habit and scapular reading from
an open book held in her right hand, on an
oval base.
6 in high

211 White figure of a sportsman *c.* 1756
in peaked cap, flowing jacket, waistcoat,
breeches and boots with a belt and satchel at
his waist, holding a dead bird in his extended
right arm and a rifle at his side, standing
before a tree-stump on a circular base with a
dog at his feet, *incised W mark.*
6¾ in high

Provenance:
Brigadier James L. Hill, sale Sotheby's,
25 March 1974, lot 208

Perhaps inspired by the Meissen model by J. F. Eberlein
of *c.* 1746

**212 A pair of figures of a sportsman
and companion** *c.* 1756
wearing black tricorn hats, pink-lined pale-
yellow jacket, a flowered waistcoat, a
flowered dress, turquoise breeches and black
boots, both holding guns with dogs at their
sides on circular scroll-moulded bases applied
with yellow-centred blue and red flowers.
8 in high

Lord Suffield, Gunton Park, sale Irelands,
16 September 1980, lot 786

Cf. Adams (Elizabeth) and David Redstone: *Bow Porcelain*,
pls. 128A & B

213 A pair of figures of cooks *c.* 1756
he in pale-blue turban, blue lined pale-yellow
jacket, white apron and pink flowered
breeches, holding a circular dish with two
birds, his companion in lace cap, pale pink-
lined yellow dress, white bodice and apron
and a flowered skirt, holding a ham, both
standing on circular pad bases applied with
flowers.
6½ in high

Cf. Hurlbutt (Frank): *Bow Porcelain*, pl. 35A, together with
Bouchardon's engraving
Lane (Arthur): *18th Century English Porcelain Figures*, pl. 50A
Rackham (Bernard): *Schreiber Collection Catalogue*, pl. 6, fig.
20
E.C.C. Exhibition Catalogue, 1948, pl. 41, nos. 169 & 170
Untermyer Collection Catalogue, pl. 81, fig. 244
Taken from Bouchardon's 'Cris de Paris'
The male figure is also recorded in Chelsea
Mentioned in the 1756 Memorandum Book of John
Bowcock where sixteen were ordered from him by a dealer
named Fogg

214

214 A pair of pugilists *c.* 1756
wearing striped pink and pale-blue breeches,
their hats and coats at their sides, standing
before tree-stumps on mound bases applied
with a red-edged yellow-centred flower with
three green leaves.
5¾ in high

Provenance:
Mrs John W. Christner, sale Christie's New
York, 8 June 1979, lot 20

There is an example in the Passmore Edwards Museum,
East London, together with a torso excavated on the
factory site in 1969
Cf. No. 235

215 216

**215 A group of a putto on a
leopard** 1756–58
scantily draped in pink with a wreath of
trailing vine in his hair, the leopard with
beige fur with grey spots, on an oval base
applied with grapes and green foliage,
impressed To mark at back.
4 in high

Cf. No. 216
There is a further example of this model in the Museum
of London that bears an incised T mark
After a Meissen model

**216 A group of Cupid seated on a
lion** 1756–58
scantily draped in a puce-lined opaque blue
robe, a yellow quiver of arrows at his feet,
the lion with curling mane, on an oval
rockwork base, *impressed To mark.*
6 in high

217

217 A group of a putto with a monkey *c.* 1756

the putto's hair dressed in a bun, and scantily draped in yellow feeding a fruit to a squatting monkey with naturally coloured fur and red mouth, on an oval base applied with blue, puce and red flowers with yellow centres surrounded by green leaves and with raised green moss, *incised T mark.*
$3\frac{1}{4}$ in high

Cf. No. 230, the chinoiserie group of which the present small group forms a part. From a Meissen model first conceived by P. Reinicke, *c.* 1745
Pauls-Eisenbeiss Collection Catalogue, vol. I, pp. 110 & 111

218 Figure of an equestrian hussar

c. 1756

in a fur-lined yellow cape and hat and pale-pink tunic, breeches and black boots, astride a yellow-edged green saddle-cloth on a prancing dappled white horse, on an oval scroll-moulded base enriched in green and puce.
$4\frac{1}{2}$ in high

Anon., sale Christie's, 23 March 1964, lot 124
Anon., sale Christie's, 16 June 1975, lot 40, there attributed to Longton Hall

219 Figure of a youth sawing a log 1756–58

in iron-red fur-lined cap, ermine-lined pale-pink jacket, pale-blue waistcoat, pale-yellow breeches with puce flowers, white stockings and black shoes, astride a pile of logs and sawing a log on a cross-stretcher on an oval base.
$5\frac{1}{2}$ in high

Cf. Hurlbutt (Frank): *Bow Porcelain*, pl. 64, fig. 1b for the Meissen original and pl. 31B for a Bow example

220 White figure of a seated flautist

c. 1755

playing his instrument wearing a cap, jacket and breeches, seated on rockwork, on a circular pad base
$3\frac{3}{4}$ in high

Provenance:
Anon., sale Sotheby's, 20 December 1972, lot 104

Cf. *E.C.C. Exhibition Catalogue, 1948*, pl. 39, no. 188
These are mentioned in *William Duesbury's London Account Book 1751–1753*, p. 5 '3pr of small flutors ... 0-6-0' and 2pr of flotars ... 0-4-0.'

218

219

220

221 Figure of a lady musician *c.* 1758
playing the lyre, in pale-yellow hat, turquoise
bodice and white skirt, painted with trailing
garden flowers and black shoes, seated on
rockwork, on a scroll-moulded base enriched
in puce with three applied flowers.
8 in high

Provenance:
Anon., sale Bonham's, 25 March 1977, lot 78

**222 Figure of a seated mandolin
player** *c.* 1758
in pale-pink hat, yellow waistcoat and white
shirt, his breeches painted with flowers,
seated on a tree-stump on a rockwork base
applied with coloured flowers with yellow-
green leaves.
6 in high

Inspired by a Meissen model by J. J. Kaendler
For a Longton Hall example, cf. Savage (George): *18th
Century English Porcelain*, pl. 80E

223 Figure of Pierrot *c.* 1758
in iron-red lined pink hat, pale yellow jacket
with gilt frogging, striped and chequer-
pattern trousers and black shoes, standing
with his arms in front of him before a tree-
stump, on a circular pad base applied with
groups of three blue, red and pink flowers.
5½ in high

Cf. Rackham (Bernard): *Schreiber Collection Catalogue*, pl. 2,
no. 21
For a Chelsea example, cf. Savage (George): *18th Century
English Porcelain*, pl. 24B
John Bowcock Memorandum Book 'May 4, 1756 ... Mr.
Williams ... I enammelled Pero,6s'

224 Figure of Summer *c.* 1758
modelled as a girl in a pink hat, pale-yellow
and black bodice, yellow skirt and flowered
apron painted with flowers in the Chelsea
style and holding a sheaf of corn, on a scroll-
moulded base enriched in puce.
6 in high

221

222

223

224

225 Figure of a shepherdess *c.* 1758
in white scarf and bodice painted with puce
flowers and tied with yellow ribbon, a florally
painted white apron and skirt, holding a posy
with applied flowers in her apron, standing
on a high puce scroll-moulded base applied
with a white recumbent sheep and coloured
double-flowers with three grey-green leaves.
10¾ in high

Provenance:
Anon., sale Sotheby's, 18 April 1967, lot 127
Anon., sale Sotheby's, 26 November 1974, lot
135

Cf. Lane (Arthur): *English Porcelain Figures of the 18th
Century*, pl. 46
Bow Porcelain Exhibition Catalogue, 1959, fig. 31, no. 101 for
the companion figure playing the bagpipes, inscribed
IB 1757

225

226 Figure of Flora *c.* 1760
the goddess turned slightly to her left, her left
arm raised, draped in a pink-wash lined pale-
yellow cloak and wearing a dress painted
with sprays of garden flowers in blue, yellow,
iron-red and puce, tied with an iron-red belt,
standing before a tree-stump on a rectangular
pale-marbled base with a carnation, a rose
and other flowers at her feet.
$17\frac{1}{2}$ in high

Cf. Lane (Arthur): *English Porcelain Figures of the 18th
Century*, pl. 52
Honey (W. B.): *Old English Porcelain*, pl. 48
It was suggested by Arthur Lane: *op. cit.*, p. 32 that this
copy of the Farnese Flora was perhaps taken from a
plaster by Scheemakers from the original Antique
However R. J. Charleston and Geoffrey Wills: 'The Bow
Flora and Michael Rysbrack', *Apollo*, LXIII, 1956, pp.
125–7, previously suggested that it was taken from a
terracotta by Rysbrack, signed and dated 1759, perhaps
using Scheemaker's plaster

227 White figure of Ceres 1760–65
the scantily draped female figure with raised
right arm, her left at her side, standing
before a sheaf of corn on a circular base.
$3\frac{1}{4}$ in high

226

227

228 Figure of Earth *c.* 1760
modelled as a nymph in a pale-pink-lined yellow cloak and flowered dress boldly painted with puce, yellow and blue flowers tied with a blue belt, holding a spirally-moulded cornucopia of fruit and flowers and standing before a lion with brown fur, chocolate muzzle and yellow eyes on an oval base applied with a blue flower with four green leaves.
$7\frac{3}{4}$ in high

Provenance:
Lord Suffield, Gunton Park, sale Irelands, 16 September 1980, lot 775

Cf. No. 245

229 Figure of Water *c.* 1760
modelled as Neptune standing in an opaque-blue lined pink robe painted with purple flowers holding an upturned jar of water painted with two flowers, standing before a green and yellow scaled dolphin with a brown tail and face, on an oval mound base enriched in blue.
$7\frac{1}{2}$ in high

Cf. No. 245

228

229

230 A chinoiserie group *c.* 1760
modelled as a magician in pale-yellow lined
pink conical hat, and flowing flowered coat
tied with a blue belt, his lady assistant in a
lime-green lined pink coat and yellow dress,
her hair tied in a bun, both flanking a
scantily draped child seated on a stool, with
a child handing an apple to a monkey in the
foreground, on a shaped oval base applied
with pink, yellow and red yellow-centred
flowers, with foliage in two tones of green.
6½ in high

After the Meissen model by P. Reinicke, first conceived in
1745
Cf. *Pauls-Eisenbeiss Collection Catalogue*, vol. I, pp. 110/111
Hurlbutt (Frank): *Bow Porcelain*, pl. 43B for a later
adaptation of this group showing only the magician,
monkey and the child on the stool and on a four-footed
base
For a group of the monkey with a putto, see No. 217

230

**231 A group emblematic of Africa and
Asia** *c.* 1762
Africa as a negress in an elephant headdress
in green bodice and blue, yellow and pink
dress with a lion at her feet, Asia in a yellow
flowered dress holding an urn standing before
a flowering tree-stump applied with yellow
and blue flowers and leaves in two tones of
green, on a shaped oval mound scroll-
moulded base enriched in puce and blue.
5¼ in high

Provenance:
Formerly in the C. R. Stephens Collection
Anon., sale Bonham's, 25 March 1977, lot 76

231

COLOUR PLATE X

232 A tea-party group *c.* 1760
modelled as a gallant and companion
flanking a marble pedestal with a vase of
flowers, he in pale-yellow frock-coat, flowered
waistcoat and yellow breeches, with a
blackamoor attendant in a washed blue
jacket, striped skirt and black breeches,
holding a tray, the lady seated beside a moss-
encrusted wall forming a fountain, a
recumbent pug-dog before them, on a shaped
oval base encrusted with flowers, *incised T
mark.*
10 in wide

Provenance:
Anon., sale Phillips, 13 May 1981, lot 81

Cf. G. A. Godden: *An Illustrated Encyclopaedia of British
Pottery and Porcelain*, fig. 69 for a similar model

232

**233 A pair of figures of seated
musicians** 1762–65
he in pink-lined yellow hat, bright-blue
jacket, yellow waistcoat and pink breeches
painted with puce flowers, playing the drum,
she in blue hat, blue-edged pink jacket and
yellow skirt edged in blue and painted with
puce flower-sprays, playing the zither, both
seated on divided boughs applied with
coloured flowers in puce, blue and yellow
with leaves in two tones of green, on four-
footed scroll-moulded bases enriched in puce
and blue, *she with impressed To mark.*
8 in high

Cf. Stoner (Frank): *Chelsea, Bow and Derby Porcelain Figures*,
pl. 78
For an earlier pair see Wallace Elliot, sale Sotheby's, 25
May 1938, lot 247

233

234 A candlestick-group *c.* 1760
emblematic of Summer, modelled as a putto
and a nymph scantily draped in dark-purple
and yellow flowered clothes, the putto with a
basket of flowers on his head, about a central
scroll-moulded support enriched in puce,
turquoise and gilding supporting a foliage-
moulded candle-nozzle, enriched in iron-red,
puce and yellow, on an oval scroll-moulded
base similarly enriched.
10½ in high

Literature:
Morley-Fletcher (Hugo): *Investing in Pottery
and Porcelain*, p. 101

Cf. Rackham (Bernard): *Schreiber Collection Catalogue*, pl. 2,
nos. 94 & 95
Taken from a Meissen original

235 Figure of a pugilist *c.* 1765
with a pale-blue scarf and grey hair, his
cheeks enriched in iron-red, his arms raised
and wearing red-striped pale-yellow breeches,
his hat and clothes resting at his side, on a
rockwork scroll-moulded base enriched in
turquoise and gilding, *anchor and dagger mark
in iron-red, blue X mark.*
6½ in high

Cf. Stoner (Frank): *Chelsea, Bow and Derby Porcelain Figures*,
pl. 98
Also No. 214 for an earlier pair

234

235

236 A pair of figures of putti *c.* 1765
each scantily clothed in a bright yellow-lined
puce cloth with a garland of garden flowers
and foliage over their shoulders and with a
garland in their hair, carrying a basket of
garden flowers, each standing before tree-
stumps on circular pad bases applied with
garden flowers in puce, yellow and blue.
6½ in high

Cf. Savage (George): *18th Century English Porcelain*, pl. 65c
Hurlbutt (Frank): *Bow Porcelain*, pl. 38b

237 Figure of Autumn *c.* 1765
modelled as Bacchus with grapes in his hair
in an underglaze-blue-lined cloak, painted
with blue and yellow flowers with gilt foliage
on a puce ground, holding a chalice and
squeezing a bunch of grapes, leaning on a
scroll-moulded baluster vase full of grapes
and painted with flowers, on a four-footed
scroll-moulded base enriched in puce,
turquoise and gilding.
10½ in high

Provenance:
Anon., sale Sotheby's, King & Chasemore,
1 November 1979, lot 1377

There are similar examples in the Bearsted Collection,
Upton House, Banbury

238 Figure of Autumn *c.* 1765
similarly modelled to the preceding but badly
warped in the firing, wearing a pink-lined
pale-yellow cloak squeezing a bunch of
grapes into a goblet and leaning on a
baluster vase of fruit, painted with a
turquoise and iron-red flower-spray enriched
with puce and turquoise scrolls, on a four-
footed scroll-moulded base enriched in puce
and encrusted with flowers.
10½ in high

Cf. No. 237

236

237

238

239 A set of four figures of The Continents *c.* 1765
Europe as Minerva in gilt scale-pattern cuirass and puce-lined robes with a shield at her side, Asia in flowered robe holding a jar, America as a Red Indian in feathered headdress and chiton with a crocodile at his feet, and Africa as a negress scantily draped in a flowered robe with an iron-red sash, a lion at her feet, all standing before flower-encrusted tree-stumps on pierced square spreading socles enriched in gilding. *Europe with iron-red anchor and dagger mark at back.* $5\frac{1}{2}$ in high

Provenance:
Anon., sale Sotheby's, 13 February 1979, lot 103

Literature:
Bradshaw (Peter): *18th Century English Porcelain Figures*, pl. 84

Cf. Savage (George): *18th Century English Porcelain*, pl. 67A and B for America and Europe
Rackham (Bernard): *Catalogue of the Herbert Allen Collection*, pl. 3, no. 9, for Europe and Africa

240 A pair of figures of Harlequin and Columbine *c.* 1765
modelled in dancing attitude wearing
brightly coloured chequered clothes, her skirt
with blue flowerheads reserved with ogival
panels of gilt foliage, both before flowering
trees applied with groups of brightly coloured
flowers in iron-red, blue, puce and gilding,
standing on three-footed scroll-moulded bases
enriched in puce and gilding, *anchor and
dagger marks in iron-red.*
7½ in high

Provenance:
Anon., sale Christie's, 16 June 1975, lot 67

Cf. Rackham (Bernard): *Schreiber Collection Catalogue*, pl. 2,
no. 198 for earlier versions of these models on pad bases

241 A pair of candlestick-figures *c.* 1765
modelled as a gallant and companion playing
the tambourine and the triangle wearing
predominently pale-yellow, puce and iron-red
flowered clothes, standing before flowering
trees applied with brightly coloured flowers
in underglaze-blue, puce, red and yellow,
supporting pierced foliage nozzles on *tôle-
peinte* supports, enriched in underglaze-blue
and gilding, on pierced scroll-moulded bases
enriched in turquoise, puce and gilding,
*underglaze blue A marks, and anchor and dagger
marks in iron-red.*
9½ in high

**242 A group of a Turk and
companion** *c.* 1765
she wearing a helmet and in ermine-lined
pink cloak and puce flowerhead-pattern
bodice and skirt, he in a white turban, yellow
flowered jacket, turquoise trousers and red
boots, standing before a flowering tree, on a
four-footed scroll-moulded base enriched in
turquoise and gilding.
7½ in high

243 A fountain-group *c.* 1765
modelled as a gallant and companion in
pale-pink and iron-red striped and flowered
clothes, standing each side of a grotto formed
from a marbled fountain with a putto's head
spouting water, standing before a tree
applied with blossom in white, pink and red
and with foliage in tones of green, on a four-
footed scroll-moulded base enriched in
gilding.
9 in high

241

242

243

244 A group of a gallant and companion *c.* 1765

from a set of The Seasons, Summer modelled as a girl with a sheaf of corn, Autumn as a man with a basket of grapes wearing predominantly underglaze-blue, turquoise and puce flowered clothes, standing before a flowering tree with bright puce, yellow and iron-red flowers, on a four-footed scroll-moulded base enriched in underglaze-blue and overglaze puce, turquoise and gilding, *underglaze blue A mark and iron-red anchor and dagger mark.*
9 in high

Provenance:
Anon., sale Bonham's, 25 March 1977, lot 118

Cf. *Untermyer Collection Catalogue*, pl. 84, fig. 252 for a similar candelabrum-group

244

245 A set of four figures emblematic of The Elements *c.* 1770

modelled as gods and goddesses in flowered robes lined in puce or turquoise, Air as a nymph with an eagle, Earth holding a cornucopia and with a lion at her feet, Fire as a youth with a brazier of coals and Water as Neptune with an upturned jar and a dolphin, all standing on high scroll-moulded bases lightly enriched in gilding, *anchor and dagger marks in iron-red to Air, Earth and Water.*
11 in high

Cf. Savage (George): *18th Century English Porcelain*, pl. 66B for Fire
E.C.C. Exhibition Catalogue, 1948, pl. 43, nos. 198–200 for earlier versions of Air, Earth and Water
Also Nos. 228 and 229

245

Animals and Birds

The Bow ménagerie and aviary mostly date from the 1750s. The earliest members are perhaps the white lions and pug-dogs, here illustrated by a white pug on an early rectangular base with incised geometric designs and a coloured companion (Nos. 246 and 247); derived from Meissen originals, the coloured example shows similar treatment in the painting to the Muses figures. The stag and hind (No. 250) show the beginnings of mound bases applied with flowers and they seem to have been popular models which reappear later in front of flowering trees. The small standing lion and lioness (No. 262) and the monkey sweetmeat-dishes (No. 254) both illustrate the development of scroll-moulded bases and date from 1758–60.

The birds, on the other hand, are here represented showing a slightly wider range of dates. The cormorant (No. 263), which is also known in white, has the incised green seaweed already noted on the early salts, similar to the white salt in the British Museum, dated 1750. However, on the evidence of palette, the cormorant would seem to be a little later. At the other end of the scale, the parrot (No. 267) on its scroll-moulded base, and the goldfinch (No. 270) on its pierced and waisted pedestal peculiar to Bow, may be considered some of the latest productions of the Bow bird series. Peter Bradshaw in his book *18th Century English Porcelain Figures, 1745–1795*, in appendices G, H and I lists over 250 figures, groups and animals (listing pairs and sets as *one* only). Of these only 27 are animals and 33 are birds, none of which seem to belong to the later period of 1765–75. This would seem to indicate that these animals and birds did not lend themselves to the elaborate scroll bases and flowering trees which are associated with the late figure models seen in the previous section.

246 White figure of a recumbent pug

c. 1752

to the right, turned slightly towards his tail with incised eyes and muzzle, on a rectangular base incised with geometric designs.

4¾ in wide

Cf. No. 247 for a coloured example

Rackham (Bernard): *Catalogue of the Schreiber Collection,* pl. 9, no. 147

246

247 Figure of a recumbent pug *c.* 1752

to the right, his head turned towards his rear and tail arched over his back, with black muzzle and brown streaked coat on a rectangular pale-green washed base, the sides incised with geometric designs.

4¾ in wide

Provenance:

Brigadier James L. Hill, sale Sotheby's, 25 March 1974, lot 214

Cf. No. 246 for a white example

247

148

248

248 Lion and lioness *c.* 1752

seated on their haunches, their manes and
tails in dark-brown, their bodies in a lighter
shade, their paws raised on tree-stumps, on
shaped green bases. [The painting perhaps of
later date]

4 in wide

Cf. Savage (George): *18th Century English Porcelain*, pl. 47A
Rackham (Bernard): *Schreiber Collection Catalogue*, pl. 9, no.
146
Adams (Elizabeth) and David Redstone: *Bow Porcelain*, pl.
123 for a white pair

249 White figure of a barking retriever

c. 1752

with raised tail and lightly incised fur, a dead
bird trapped beneath its right foot, on a
rectangular mound base applied with a twig
and a flowerhead beneath a rich creamy
glaze.

4 in long

Provenance:
Brigadier James L. Hill, sale Sotheby's, 6
December 1977, lot 13

Cf. Rackham (Bernard): *Schreiber Collection Catalogue*, pl. 9,
no. 701

249

250

251

**250 A pair of figures of a recumbent
stag and hind** 1755–56
with brown dappled hides on oval bases
applied with coloured flowers and three
green leaves, *both with painter's numeral 2.*
3½ in long

Provenance:
The Hon. Mrs B. Bruce, sale Sotheby's,
9 November 1976, lot 79

**251 A pair of white figures of a lion and
lioness** 1753–55
prowling to left and right, their tails between
their back legs and bearing fierce expressions,
on oval rockwork bases.
9 in long

Provenance:
Anon., sale Sotheby's, 25 January 1977, lot
64

Cf. *E.C.C. Commemorative Exhibition Catalogue 1977*, fig. 138
for a similar pair

252 A group of a ewe and lamb 1752–54
the ewe recumbent to the left and turned
towards her lamb asleep across her hind
quarters, their faces in a light brown and
with black hoofs and muzzles, on an oval
rockwork base applied with blue and red
yellow-centred flowers with yellow-green
foliage.
4½ in long

Provenance:
Anon., sale Christie's, 25 October 1976, lot
170, there attributed to Derby

Cf. Hurlbutt (Frank): *Bow Porcelain*, pl. 1, for a white
example
Savage (George): *18th Century English Porcelain*, pl. 46c for
a similar model
This is also known in Derby, English pottery and
delftware

253 A pair of cats *c.* 1758
seated to left and right, their coats with pale-
puce fur markings and with lemon-yellow
eyes, on oval bases with puce scrolls.
2½ in high

Cf. Adams (Elizabeth) and David Redstone: *Bow Porcelain*,
pl. 135 for a similar example
E.C.C. Exhibition Catalogue, 1948, pl. 39, no. 193 for an
example with a mouse

252

253

254 A pair of sweetmeat-dishes *c.* 1758
modelled as male and female monkeys
wearing a deep-red and yellow waistcoat and
striped trousers, his companion in a yellow-
edged pink jacket and flowered skirt, seated
before shell-moulded pierced bowls painted
with blue, yellow and puce flowers on scroll-
moulded bases enriched in puce and blue.
5½ in high

Cf. Stoner (Frank): *Chelsea, Bow and Derby Porcelain Figures*,
pl. 106 for a similar pair, the female with an incised T
mark

COLOUR PLATE IX
255 Figure of a dismal hound *c.* 1758
to the right, its coat with brown markings
and with red tongue, seated on an oval base
painted with a puce and red flower, with
grey-green leaves and with two other flower-
sprays.
3¼ in high

Provenance:
Mrs B. Sargeant, sale Phillips, 22 November
1978, lot 106

Cf. *E.C.C. Exhibition Catalogue, 1948*, pl. 39, no. 194
Adams (Elizabeth) and David Redstone: *Bow Porcelain*, pl.
129 for a pair with applied flowers to the bases

256 Figure of a hare *c.* 1760
in pale brown, seated on its haunches and
scratching its left ear, on an oval base
enriched in dark-puce.
3½ in high

Provenance:
Anon., sale Christie's, 9 February 1981, lot
229

254

255

256

257 Figure of a recumbent cow *c.* 1760
to the left with brown hide markings, its tail
arched over its left flank, on an oval base
applied with pale-yellow, blue and puce
flowers with grey-green leaves.
3¼ in long

**258 A pair of figures of a cow and
bull** *c.* 1760
their hides mottled in tones of grey and
brown, supported by tree-trunks on oval
bases applied with blue, puce and iron-red
flowers with yellow centres, surrounded by
five green leaves.
the cow 6 in long
the bull 6¼ in long

Provenance:
Mrs J. Walter Wyles, executor's sale
Sotheby's, 10 May 1955, lot 144
Nelson Rockefeller, sale Sotheby's New York,
11 April 1980, lot 54

Cf. Stoner (Frank): *Chelsea, Bow and Derby Porcelain Figures*,
pl. 104
Adams (Elizabeth) and David Redstone: *Bow Porcelain*, pl.
121

257

258

259 White figure of a seated fox *c.* 1760
his left forepaw resting on a tree-stump, on a
round pad base.
1½ in high

The attribution of this example remains uncertain

COLOUR PLATE IX
260 Figure of two monkeys *c.* 1760
modelled as a crouching monkey with red
mouth, a young monkey on its back, both
with their arms raised to their eyes, their
coats in natural colours, on a circular mound
base applied with a flower and three leaves.
3 in high

Provenance:
Brigadier James L. Hill, sale Sotheby's, 25
March 1974, lot 206

261 Two figures of standing pugs
c. 1760
to left and right, with brown fur markings,
their tails arched over their backs, their
muzzles and eyes enriched in black, wearing
a blue and yellow collar on oval scroll-
moulded bases enriched in puce.
2 ¼ in high

Provenance:
Brigadier James L. Hill, sale Sotheby's, 6
December 1977, lots 8 & 9

**262 A pair of figures of a lion and
lioness** *c.* 1760
to left and right, their coats in natural
colours, their muzzles in grey with yellow
eyes, standing on rectangular scroll-moulded
bases enriched in puce and blue, a blue
flower with a yellow centre and green foliage
beneath them, *the lion with impressed E mark.*
2 in long

Provenance:
Anon., sale Christie's, 21 March 1977, lot
155

259   260

261

262

263 Figure of a cormorant 1752–56
with outstretched wings, its plumage in tones
of grey and brown with slightly incised wing
and tail feathers, standing on a circular
rockwork mound applied with shells, two fish
and seaweed.
3½ in high

Provenance:
Anon., sale Christie's, 19 June 1978, lot 213

Cf. *Untermyer Collection Catalogue*, pl. 92, fig. 307

263

264 Duck tureen and cover 1755–56
naturally modelled, to the right, with yellow
beak, brown head, black eyes and brown and
dark-purple feathers.
4½ in long

Provenance:
Anon., sale Sotheby's, 21 February 1947, lot
23
James MacHarg, sale Sotheby's, 14 May
1974, lot 158

Exhibited:
E.C.C. Commemorative Exhibition Catalogue, 1977,
no. 133

Cf. *Untermyer Collection Catalogue*, pl. 10, fig. 20
Taken from George Edwards: *Natural History of Uncommon
Birds*, vol. III, pl. 157, described as 'Little Brown and
White Ducks'
There is a pair in the Temple Newsam Museum, Leeds,
one with similar colouring to the present example, the
other in tones of sepia

264

265 A pair of birds of prey *c.* 1758
their heads turned towards their right wings,
with yellow breasts, red necks and purple,
pink and yellow wing and tail feathers,
astride tree-stumps on circular mound bases.
3 in high

Provenance:
Anon., sale Christie's, 21 April 1980, lot 146
(on Mennecy pedestals)

265

COLOUR PLATE IX
**266 A pair of figures of a cock and
hen** *c.* 1758
with red wattles and combs, their plumage
sparsely picked out in brown, blue, black and
red, on mound bases applied with yellow,
puce and blue flowerheads and green leaves.
the hen 3½ in high
the cockerel 4¼ in high

Provenance:
Lady Ludlow

Cf. *Untermyer Collection Catalogue*, pl. 92, fig. 256
Adams (Elizabeth) and David Redstone: *Bow Porcelain*, pl.
131 for the cock and hen as a single group

266

267 Figure of a South American parrot 1758–60
with blue, yellow and puce head plumage,
green breast and wing feathers and blue,
yellow and puce tail feathers, turned slightly
to the right, its right talon holding a fruit,
standing astride a tree-stump applied with
three yellow-centred blue flowers with green
foliage, on a three-footed, scroll-moulded
circular base enriched in puce.
7 in high

Provenance:
Anon., sale Christie's, 20 June 1977, lot 169

Cf. Rackham (Bernard): *Schreiber Collection Catalogue*, pl. 1,
no. 227
Savage (George): *18th Century English Porcelain*, pl. 118
Stoner (Frank): *Chelsea, Bow and Derby Porcelain Figures*, pl.
111 for a similar example
From a Meissen model first conceived by J. J. Kaendler in
1741

267

268 A pair of buntings 1756–58
preening their white wings, their plumage in
tones of puce, blue and pale-yellow, standing
astride tree-stumps with red and blue flowers
with grey-green foliage, on circular mound
bases.
2½ in high

Cf. *Untermyer Collection Catalogue*, pl. 87, fig. 257
A similar example in the Eckstein Collection, sale
Sotheby's, 29 March 1949, lot 79
Stoner (Frank): *Chelsea, Bow and Derby Porcelain Figures*,
pl. 107

269 Figure of a goldfinch *c.* 1765
with iron-red and black head, brown breast
and back and black wing and tail feathers,
perched astride a flowering tree with yellow,
puce and red flowers with foliage in grey and
yellow-green on a circular three-footed scroll-
moulded base enriched in puce.
4¾ in high

Provenance:
Anon., sale Christie's, 20 June 1977, lot 167

270 Figure of a goldfinch *c.* 1765
with brown breast and upper back, yellow
and black wings and tail feathers and black
and iron-red head, standing astride a tree-
stump with coloured yellow, puce and blue
flowers on a pierced square pedestal lightly
enriched in puce and turquoise.
5¼ in high

Cf. Adams (Elizabeth) and David Redstone: *Bow Porcelain*,
pl. 134

268

269

270

Bibliography

Adams (Elizabeth)	'The Bow Insurances and Related Matters', *E.C.C. Transactions*, vol. 9, pt. 1, 1973
	'Ceramic Insurances in the Sun Company Archives', *E.C.C. Transactions*, vol. 10, pt. 1, 1976
	Some Links Between Porcelain Factories of the 18th Century and the North West of England, privately printed, 1969
Adams (Elizabeth) and David Redstone	*Bow Porcelain*, London 1981
Bemrose (William)	*Bow, Chelsea and Derby Porcelain*, London 1898
Bradshaw (Peter)	*18th Century English Porcelain Figures 1745–1795*, Woodbridge 1981
Burton (William)	*A History & Description of English Porcelain*, London 1902
Chaffers (William)	*Marks & Monograms on European & Oriental Pottery & Porcelain*, vol. 2, 15th revised edition, London 1965
Chaffers (William)	*The New Keramic Gallery*, 2 vols. revised and edited by H. M. Cundall, London 1926
Cook (Cyril)	*The Life and Work of Robert Hancock*, London 1948 Supplement to the above, London 1955
Dixon (J. L.)	*English Porcelain of the 18th Century*, London 1952
English Porcelain Circle	*Transactions* 1928–1932
English Ceramic Circle	*Transactions* 1933–
Fisher (Stanley)	*English Blue & White Porcelain of the 18th Century*, London 1947
Godden (Geoffrey A.)	*An Illustrated Encyclopaedia of British Pottery & Porcelain*, London 1966
	Oriental Export Market Porcelain, London 1979
Guest (Montague J.) ed.	*Lady Charlotte Schreiber's Journals 1869–1885*, 2 vols., London 1911
Hackenbroch (Yvonne)	*Chelsea and Other English Porcelain, Pottery and Enamel in the Irwin Untermyer Collection*, London 1957
Hobson (R. L.)	*Catalogue of The Collection of English Porcelain … in the British Museum*, London 1905
Honey (William Bowyer)	*Dresden China*, London 1934
	French Porcelain, 2nd edition, London 1972
	Old English Porcelain, 1977 edition
Hurlbutt (Frank)	*Bow Porcelain*, London 1926
Jewitt (Llewellynn)	*The Ceramic Art of Great Britain*, London 1878
King (William)	*Chelsea Porcelain*, London 1922
	English Porcelain Figures of the Eighteenth Century, London 1925
Lane (Arthur)	*English Porcelain Figures of the Eighteenth Century*, London 1961
Litchfield (Frederick)	*Pottery & Porcelain, A Guide to Collectors*, revised by Frank Tilley, 5th edition, London 1951
MacAlister (Mrs Donald) ed.	*William Duesbury's London Account Book 1751–1753*, London 1930
Mackenna (F. Severne)	*18th Century English Porcelain*, Leigh-on-Sea 1970
Morley-Fletcher (Hugo)	*Investing in Pottery & Porcelain*, London 1968

Nightingale (J. E.)	*Contributions Towards the History of Early English Porcelain*, 1973 edition
Pauls-Eisenbeiss (Dr Erika)	*German Porcelain of the 18th Century*, vol. I (*Meissen from the beginning until 1760*) London 1972
Rackham (Bernard)	*Catalogue of The Schreiber Collection of English Porcelain, Earthenware, Enamels etc. in the Victoria & Albert Museum*, vol. I, London 1915
	Catalogue of The Herbert Allen Collection of English Porcelain in the Victoria & Albert Museum, 2nd edition, London 1923
Ruckert (Rainer)	*Meissener Porzellan, 1710–1810*, München 1966
Savage (George)	*18th Century English Porcelain*, London 1952
	Porcelain Through the Ages, Penguin, London 1954
Shaw (Simeon)	*History of the Staffordshire Potteries* ... Hanley 1829
Smith (John T.)	*Nollekens and his Times*, vols. 1 and 2, 2nd edition, London 1829
Stoner (Frank)	*Chelsea, Bow and Derby Porcelain Figures*, Newport 1955
Tait (Hugh)	'The Bow Factory Under Alderman Arnold and Thomas Frye (1747–1759)', *E.C.C. Transactions*, vol. 5, pt. 4, 1963
Tilley (Frank)	*Teapots and Tea*, Newport 1957
Watney (Dr Bernard)	*English Blue & White Porcelain of the 18th Century*, 2nd edition, London 1973
	'Notes on Bow Transfer-Printing', *E.C.C. Transactions*, vol. 8, pt. 2, 1972

Articles

Apollo	Ainslie (J. A.) 'Inscribed and Dated Bow', January 1955
	Charleston (R. J.) and Geoffrey Wills vol. LXIII, 'The Bow Flora and Michael Rysbrack', 1956
	Tait (Hugh) 'Some Consequences of the Bow Special Exhibition' pt. I, 'The Alderman Arnold Period (Nov. 1748–Mar. 1750)', February 1960
	pt. II, 'The Thomas Frye Period (Sept. 1750–Apr. 1759)', April 1960
	pt. III, 'The Alderman Arnold and Thomas Frye Period (1749–1759)', June 1960
	pt. IV, 'Thomas Frye and a Rival Factory in Bow', October 1960
Burlington Magazine	Toppin (Aubrey J.) vol. XL, 'Bow Porcelain, Some Recent Excavations', May 1922
	vol. LIV, 'Some Early Bow Muses', April 1929
Connoisseur	Rackham (Bernard) vol. LXXVIII, 'Mr. Wallace Elliot's Collection of English Porcelain', June 1927
	Wills (Geoffrey) vol. CXXXIII, 'The Bow China Factory and Edward Heylyn', 1954

Exhibition Catalogues

Antique Porcelain Company
Ltd

Exhibition of English & Continental Porcelain of the 18th Century, June
1951

British Museum

Bow Porcelain 1744–1776, A Special Exhibition of Documentary
Material to commemorate the bi-centenary of the retirement of
Thomas Frye, Hugh Tait, 1959

English Ceramic Circle

*English Pottery & Porcelain. Commemorative Catalogue for an
Exhibition Held at the Victoria & Albert Museum, 5th May–20th June,
1948*, London 1949

Exhibition Catalogue 1977, R. J. Charleston & Donald Towner:
English Ceramics 1580–1830

Klaber & Klaber

Oriental Influences on European Porcelain, April 1978

Stoke on Trent City Museum
and Art Gallery, Hanley

Bow Porcelain, 14th September–31st October 1981

Stoner and Evans

Old English Porcelain, November 1909

Upton House, Banbury

The Bearsted Collection, edited by John Mallett, National Trust
1964

Winifred Williams

Eighteenth Century European White Porcelain, June 1975

Documents Cited

British Museum
(Add. Mss. 45905)

Bow Account Book 1751–1755
Bowcock Papers

Stoke on Trent City Museum
and Art Gallery, Hanley

Original Letter from John Wedgwood to Weatherby &
Crowther, re. Briand

Index